The University
AT THE CROSSROADS

Addresses & Essays

By HENRY E. SIGERIST, M.D., D.Litt., LL.D.

*William H. Welch Professor of the History of
Medicine, The Johns Hopkins University*

Henry Schuman   *New York:* 1946

PRINTED IN THE UNITED STATES OF AMERICA
BY J. J. LITTLE & IVES COMPANY, NEW YORK

To

ALAN GREGG

IN

ADMIRATION AND GRATITUDE

Preface

WHEN I was young I always felt sorry for the professors who published their collected addresses and essays instead of writing new ones. I thought that this was a certain symptom of decrepitude. And now I seem to have reached that stage myself and my young colleagues will feel sorry for me, although I must say that they are primarily responsible for this book. It was at their suggestion that I decided to collect a number of addresses and essays written during the war years, from 1939 to 1945, and to publish them as a book. Still, I feel that a word of justification is needed, particularly at a moment when the market is flooded with books on education.

The mere fact that so many studies have recently been written on the subject of the university shows that there is a problem, one about which many people feel very keenly. Research and higher education are never static, or at least should never be static, because society evolves constantly, raising new problems and making new demands on its educated citizens. The university as the nation's center of research and training must, therefore, keep on the alert continually if it wishes to lead as it should, and not merely to trail behind the trends.

A great deal of vision and foresight is needed to keep the university alive even in times of peace and prosperity. In a period of transition when the world is passing through one of its greatest crises and all values are revaluated, the university as the nation's most sensitive instrument is the first to reflect the disturbed conditions and to be affected by them. The disintegrating forces that are assailing it from all sides are endless, but at the same time the present crisis is presenting it with possibilities of regeneration and rejuvenation as never before. The university truly is at the crossroads and it depends on us whether it will emerge from this crisis as the gravedigger of an old and rotten world, or as the obstetrician of a new and better world.

It is no wonder, therefore, that all those of us who hold responsible positions in a university and are deeply concerned about the future, should raise their voices and shout loudly so as to stir up public opinion. Fearless analysis of the situation and pitiless self-criticism are needed if we wish to find the path into the future.

Preface

Not only the university at large but all its constituent parts are deeply affected by the present critical situation. And since I happen to be a physician, member of a medical faculty, I obviously am concerned about the future of the medical school also. Great technical progress has been achieved in medicine during the last twenty-five years, but the social progress has been incomparably smaller. A vast and important field of research, the sociology and economics of medicine, has been thoroughly neglected by the medical school, and medical education has hardly taken any notice of the changed technological and social conditions, and still follows a pattern that was established in this country fifty years ago. The medical school is at the crossroads also.

I am not an expert on education, and my only credential is that I have spent the last thirty-five years in universities, on three continents, in five countries, as a student first, then as an academic teacher, of graduate students mostly but sometimes also of undergraduates. I have heard of streamlined methods of education but I personally have no method, or only a very primitive one that consists of thinking aloud and having students participate in my own research work. I always found the contact with them extremely stimulating to me, but I do not know how much they benefited by my instruction. This I know, however, that I have remained in close touch with very many of my former students and that some of them have become my closest friends.

The following addresses and essays were delivered and written on various occasions, while the world was aflame and we were all working under great pressure. They obviously cannot exhaust the subject. Their intention is rather to formulate some of the major problems of the university that the war has rendered more acute than ever, and to outline some possible solutions.

Two of these essays are published here for the first time (1 and 11), one was published in *Science* (12), while the others were written for the *Bulletin of the History of Medicine,* a journal that has a limited circulation so that they have reached only a small and rather specialized group of readers.

Henry E. Sigerist

The Johns Hopkins Institute
of the History of Medicine
April 1, 1945.

Contents

Contents

THE UNIVERSITY AT THE CROSSROADS

I

Failure of a Generation

I THINK we should be honest and should admit that our generation, my generation, the one that was mature between the two World Wars, has done a miserable job. The historians who some day will write the history of our period will brand us as having been conceited, stupid and cowardly beyond measure.

We did the wrong thing whenever we had a decision to make. We went into the first World War with a great deal of idealism, sincerely believing that it was a war to end wars, one that would bring more freedom and more democracy to the people of the world, but when the peace failed we accepted the fact without rebellion. President Wilson's fourteen points, the hope and gospel of millions, were buried while jazz bands played. We went through a period of unprecedented economic boom making money without working for it, speculating merrily and we said we were abolishing poverty.

Overnight we found ourselves in a man-made world economic depression and accepted it with resignation as a natural catastrophe. Millions of people suffered the agony of unemployment; breadlines formed in the cities and we slaughtered pigs and ploughed wheat under the soil. And when the Government did a courageous far-sighted piece of work, creating, e.g., the Tennessee Valley Authority, people howled over the waste of taxpayers' money.

We watched the rise of fascism and did not move a finger. When Mussolini yelled his speeches from the balcony of Palazzo Venezia we thought it was an act in a musical comedy. When he bombed Corfu, seized Albania, invaded Ethiopia we did not worry because after all it was so far away. And did not the Italian railroads run on time, some at least? Had he not drained the Pontine marshes?

When Hitler in a Bierkeller made his impassionate speeches driving his audience into a frenzy, we thought he was a clown or at best a revivalist. We refused to be excited when he assumed power, organized and disciplined the entire nation. The Germans had always liked uniforms, and parades, and brassbands. Why should they not

Written in 1945.

have them? He slaughtered the Jews, but were the Jews not all communists? Or bankers? Whichever you like? Besides, they were his own Jews and, therefore, not our concern. Was he not erecting a bulwark against communism? Why listen to the Cassandra voice of our Ambassador Dodd, who after all was just a historian, a former college professor?

We were not only fools but cowards. Never did history develop with more iron logic, like a mathematical example, two and two are four, fascism and imperialism are war, are death and destruction, for you and me, for all of us. I do not think that it happened before that gangsters wrote books and made speeches about the crimes they intended to commit. It was so unusual that we refused to believe them. When they tested their weapons and methods in Spain, we helped them by boycotting Spain. When the airforce of the Condor Legion made an experiment in total warfare at Guernica, an experiment that was analyzed and widely discussed in the German military literature, we refused to believe that this was merely a dress-rehearsal and that one of the next cities to be bombed would be London. The British Government pretended to have no information about German troops operating in Spain. And yet they sang loud enough for the world to hear: "We are German legionaries; we fly victorious over all frontiers."

At Geneva, Litvinov never tired appealing to the peace-loving nations, urging them to join in order to meet the growing menace through collective security action. Litvinov is one of the few statesmen in the world who can afford to reprint the speeches he made ten years ago without being ashamed of himself. We refused to listen, and refusing to act accepted the war as inevitable.

Every child could have foreseen what was coming, but we had not the courage to go before the people and tell them what was in store for them, urging them to arm to the teeth in order to be ready for the test. Nobody wanted war in the democratic countries, and the politician who would have dared to tell the people that we had accepted war through inaction would never have been reelected. And so he kept quiet and through his inertia continued to encourage the fascist forces, in Europe as well as in Asia.

It was quite obvious that Japan's imperialist ambitions would lead to a conflict with the United States. The Far-Eastern Co-Prosperity

Sphere was to be dominated by Japan and had no room for American capital. And yet we thought it would and therefore helped Japan. I shall never forget the discussion I had on the subject with a big industrialist in 1940. I mentioned quite candidly that I did not consider it wise for us to supply Japan with the raw materials needed for the war against China since it might turn ultimately against us. His immediate answer was that we were acting quite correctly. "China," he said, "is an enormous potential market. The time is over when you could go and conquer a foreign country. We should be grateful that Japan is doing the dirty work for us. When she has conquered China she will be exhausted. We shall supply the capital and will exploit China in partnership with Japan."

I do not know how many people thought along that line, but we acted as if we all did and refused to fortify Guam. We talked of quarantining the aggressor and continued to supply him with the materials he needed for aggression. We established a license system for exports to Japan and increased our exports under the cover of this system. When Japan finally returned some of the scrap iron we had sold them, we were surprised and the world agreed that we had not been very clever.

Some individuals who were accustomed to think in historical terms saw more clearly what was happening but all they did was write articles, make speeches, sign manifestos. They did not act and continued with their daily work and were satisfied with it.

We did not start the war. We did not attack our neighbors. We did not build death factories in Maidanek. But we failed to prevent a catastrophe that intelligence and courage could have prevented. And now we are paying the price for this failure. After the misery of the depression we, and our children particularly, are suffering the misery of the war.

We must not look for scapegoats but must at least have the courage to admit that we failed, you and I and all of us, who make public opinion in a democratic country, who freely elect the men whom we entrust with the destinies of the nation. Men of our generation are still in responsible positions. Many of us who miserably failed yesterday will have an important voice in shaping the world of tomorrow. Unless we are fully aware of the mistakes we made, we can not hope to act more intelligently in the future, and the young

[5]

generation returning from the hell that is war, will be justified in cursing us for what we did to them.

*

It seems to me that our universities have a large share in the responsibility for the chaotic conditions of our time. The universities are supposed to train the élite of the nation. That does not mean that leaders may not arise who have never seen a campus. As a matter of fact, some of our finest labor, farm, business and political leaders have never sat between the walls of a college. They went through a different, much harder school, and the scars of life are their degrees.

Nevertheless we are justly proud of the fact that an increasing number of young men and women have the possibility of spending some of their formative years in the detached atmosphere of a university, removed from the competitive struggle for material goods, in a community of fellow students, in close touch with scholars and scientists who have devoted their life to the advancement of knowledge, in a world in which spiritual goods are highly valued.

The college years are a pause in the individual's life. After the routine of the school years and before entering upon a business or professional career, the student is granted a number of years during which he has the time and leisure to look around, to explore the physical and social world in which he lives, to study its development, its literary and artistic manifestations; time to think and read and discuss matters with his fellow students and teachers, groping for a philosophy, for a way of life, searching for the place that he wants to fill in society. The university gives him time and the opportunity to test his aptitudes in various activities, to apply his talents to various endeavors. Time and opportunity, the exposure to the challenging and provoking thought and criticism of teachers, these are the essential features of a college program. Curricula are of secondary importance, and the worst that can befall a university is acceleration in any form because no method has yet been devised to accelerate creative thinking.

The university has graduate schools which must impart the knowledge and skills required for the exercise of professions. The original structure of the Western university in four faculties has been greatly expanded, and today many universities are huge conglomera-

tions of schools including those of home economics and hotel administration. This was a development peculiar to America. Europe has
also schools for the training of farmers, and cooks, and hotel administrators but kept them separate from the university, and the USSR
went even so far as to make the medical schools independent
institutions.

We decided to make all these schools organic parts of the Universitas litterarum. Why not? It is a democratic approach to the
various vocations. One is certainly worth the other. Brillat-Savarin
demonstrated long ago that cooking is not only an art but a science,
one that has a philosophy also. Why should a cook not have an academic degree?

The inclusion of vocational schools into the university was a step
that had great implications. It meant that we were determined to raise
vocational education to academic standards. The farmer and engineer
graduating not from a technical school but from a university were to
be not only good practical farmers or engineers but highly educated
citizens fully aware of the social and philosophical implications of
their profession and prepared for leadership in the life of the nation.

When we look at the developments that took place in the last
twenty-five years, we must admit that the universities failed miserably
in their tasks. They did not produce the enlightened leaders that the
country so urgently needed. They produced legions of highly competent technicians and specialists but men without education, imbued
with traditional prejudices, unable to think independently outside
of their narrow specialty, and frequently quite indifferent toward
public affairs. Thus the inclusion of vocational schools into the university did not raise the cultural standard of the professions but
actually lowered academic standards.

After the last war money was easily available and the universities received a large share of the new wealth. It was a fictitious prosperity, to be sure, but much money was in circulation and as long as
it lasted it could be invested for good purposes. Many excellent and
much needed reforms were carried out. Out-moded medical schools
were closed or reorganized. New departments were created. But as
a whole the universities grew in width and not in depth. Millions
were invested in spectacular buildings until the campus of some
universities reached the size of a small town. Institutes were some-

times founded not because they were particularly needed but because they seemed to be good "selling propositions," projects that would appeal to the men who controlled funds and therefore would bring money to the university. Other institutions were founded with utterly inadequate means on the speculation that more funds would come forth sometime in the future. Many of them collapsed or never outgrew the embryonic stage when the depression set in, and all universities found it difficult to operate their greatly increased plants.

The physical growth of the schools created great administrative problems. Presidents, deans, heads of departments were no longer educators but executive officers. Many liked their new position, but education suffered. Instead of producing creative ideas, they produced elaborate curricula with complicated coordination schemes and a system of grading students that required higher mathematics. Graduate education suffered particularly. Buildings could be erected from gifts, but the operation of the schools was dependent on steady income. Hence, universities were anxious to increase the number not of their graduate but of their under-graduate students and tried to attract them with more buildings, luxurious dormitories, gymnasiums, clubhouses.

Universities also failed in many ways in their other task, in the promotion and cultivation of research. They produced the tools for research but not the men to use them. There was no lack of fellowships for "promising young men" but when a student was in any way unusual either because his field of study was out of the ordinary or because his career had been unorthodox, he frequently did not meet with the requirements of a fellowship program, requirements that were set for average students. And those who succeeded in obtaining highly specialized training under a fellowship were frequently dropped as soon as they began to fulfill the promise of their youth or were forced to accept positions that made it impossible or at least very difficult for them to continue with their researches.

Nobody will deny that some very important contributions to knowledge came from universities during the last twenty-five years, but they were made primarily in the technical fields, in physics, chemistry, medicine, engineering, agriculture, and some of the most important work was done outside of the universities, in independent research institutions and government laboratories. The humanities, and to a certain extent the social sciences also, became the stepchildren of the university. The trend was toward utilitarianism. Philosophy, the mother of all sciences and the connecting link between them all, was pushed into the background.

Many fields of research of vital importance to the nation were not touched at all, either because they were controversial or because they seemed to have no immediate practical value. This failure was to a large extent caused by the financial structure of the university. The endowed universities are administered by self-perpetuating Boards of Trustees, the members of which are recruited from a very small group of the population. Neither labor nor the farmers are represented on them; neither the educators nor the researchers. This one-sided selection obviously limits the field of action of the Boards considerably, and their primary function has become the financial administration of the institution and the raising of funds to meet its increasing demands. The trustees, therefore, must see to it that their university does not undertake any projects that might give offense to potential donors. It happens, however, that some of the most vital issues of our time, issues that determine war and peace, misery and prosperity are highly controversial and that research in these fields might yield results that could be offensive to potential donors who are also to be found only in a very small group of the population.

While it probably is easy to convince trustees of the value of a laboratory of industrial research, it is more difficult to persuade them to provide funds for a strong Greek department, or for the study of African languages or of Chinese philosophy.

In state universities funds have to be appropriated by the legislature, and it is obvious that these bodies are not exempt from ignorance and prejudice that may restrict the university in its tasks. Legislative assemblies, however, are democratically elected bodies and in states in which public opinion is progressive and enlightened, universities have been fully supported without political interference.

The structure of our universities puts a tremendous responsibility on the president. He is the link between faculty and administrative board. He has great power, and if he is a leader and has a cultural policy he can be a constant source of inspiration to the faculty and a guide to the board.

*

[9]

The University at the Crossroads

The young generation that grew up during the years of depression, is on the battlefields today while we, the failures of yesterday who drove them into the war through lack of foresight, are at home holding all the important positions of the country. Some day they will come back, no longer children but men and women matured by years of hardship and suffering. They will refuse to accept wars and depressions as natural catastrophes and will force us to render them an account of our past and present actions.

What shall we do? We must atone not by shedding useless tears but by making an honest effort to act more intelligently. We must have the courage to admit the mistakes we made, and, working hand in hand with the young generation that will take over in the near future, we must endeavor to create better conditions. We must stop treating symptoms of evils when we know their cause, unpleasant as this knowledge may be to some of us. Safety devices are necessary when our basement is full of dynamite, and international conferences can spend a great deal of time discussing various models of safety valves. But it would be better to throw the dynamite into the river.

Intelligent action requires educated people and knowledge that is the result of research. Our universities, therefore, still have an extremely important part to play. They have failed in many respects and are threatened with destruction from many sides. Fearless analysis and bold new departures are needed, if we wish to save the university and to make it the nervous system of the nation that perceives developments and trends, thinks, and from which impulses for intelligent action arise. It is the duty of all those of us who are responsible members of universities to atone for past failures by working toward that end.

2

University Education

Mr. Chairman of the Council
Mr. Principal
Ladies and Gentlemen,

I am deeply moved and I wish to express my profound gratitude for the great honor bestowed upon me by the University of the Witwatersrand. Sometimes I feel that honorary degrees are somewhat like arteriosclerosis, a symptom of the beginning of old age. You have worked assiduously for a long time. You are getting on in years. Your arteries begin to harden and your work to be recognized. But then, of course, there is a great difference in that arteriosclerosis is a most unpleasant symptom while the recognition of a man's work is the strongest encouragement he can possibly find and the most powerful incentive to pursue in his endeavours. And for an academic teacher there is no higher distinction than to be admitted among the honorary graduates of a university.

In honoring me you have at the same time expressed your appreciation of the field of research to which I have devoted my life's work. And since it is unusual for a physician to study the history and sociology of medicine, let me tell you how I became interested in the subject and let me pay tribute to the memory of some great teachers it was my good fortune to have. If I have been able to make a contribution to my field of studies—modest as it may be—it was due to hard work, without which nothing is ever achieved, but also and to a large extent to the inspiration I received from great teachers.

I have to go far back to recall the figure of the first teacher who had a profound influence on the formation of my mind. When, in 1901, my family moved from Paris to Zurich, in Switzerland, I was ten years old, and since I had a very imperfect knowledge of German I was sent not to a public but to a private school. It was owned and directed by an educator of genius, *Fritz von Beust*. Son of a German

An Address delivered in Johannesburg, South Africa, on November 15, 1939 on the occasion of the conferment of the degree of Doctor of Literature *honoris causa* by the University of the Witwatersrand.

revolutionary who after 1848 had sought asylum in Zurich and opened a progressive school, he followed in the footsteps of his father. A strong man with a pink face and white beard, he was a convinced socialist and atheist and was first of all an enthusiastic scientist. Science played a dominating part in the curriculum. The rotation of the earth was demonstrated to the children by having them build a sundial in the garden and watching it through the seasons. We learned geometry by making cubes, cones and other bodies. In geography we pasted maps on cardboard, dissected the various altitude layers with the jig saw and mounted them so as to construct relief maps of the country. And every few weeks we made whole-day excursions into the beautiful surroundings of Zurich. The geography of the region was discussed but the chief purpose was to collect plants. Each one of us had a herbarium, and at the age of twelve we had learned to analyze the structure of plants and were able to diagnose the family of every one of them. A most liberal spirit pervaded the school. Teachers and students were carried away by von Beust's personality whose mere presence was sufficient to insure discipline. He opened up for me the realm of nature and awakened in me as in so many others a deep interest in science. It was only much later that I realized how much the three years spent in that school had influenced my whole outlook. After von Beust's death the school was continued for a few years by his co-workers but the driving spirit was gone and the school closed down. It could afford to do so because in the meantime the public schools had adopted most of its principles.

In 1904 I became a student of the *Gymnasium* in Zurich. It was a public school preparing boys from all classes of society for academic studies. I was in the humanistic division where for six and a half years we had eight hours of Latin and for five and a half years eight hours of Greek a week, so that at the end of the course most of us could read Latin and some of us also Greek fluently. In spite of the emphasis on the classics, modern languages were not neglected. French was a required subject all through the course and we had a choice between English and Italian. In addition we had excellent instruction in science which proves that it is quite possible to combine science with humanistic studies.

Among the many teachers I had during that period one stands out far above all the others: our professor of history, *Otto Markwart*.

He was not a detached but a passionate historian, violent in his sympathies and antipathies. He worshipped Mozart and loathed Wagner. A student of Jakob Burckhardt he was a humanist, deeply attached to Italy where he spent his vacation every year, returning with piles of photographs that he passed around in the classes. An enthusiastic teacher he could electrify the students. Discussing a stormy session of the Roman Senate he jumped up addressing the class: "You are the Roman Senate. What are you going to do? You have defeated Carthage but again she raises her head threateningly. You there in the corner are Cato. Get up and tell them what they shall do!" And the boy, Cato himself, addressed the "Senate" passionately, ending his harangue with the ominous *Ceterum censeo.* . . .

From Markwart I learned what history is—not a dead subject but a living force that determines our life. He taught us to think in terms of historic forces and developments. And in his broad approach to history that embraced all aspects of civilization he passed on to us boys the teachings of his master Jakob Burckhardt whose classical books we devoured.

The old Gymnasium in Zurich was a great school to which I owe infinitely more than I was aware at the time. It had a great tradition of liberalism and all philosophies were represented among the faculty. It taught us how to organize our work and succeeded in challenging us and arousing our intellectual curiosity so that we could spend whole nights discussing Plato, Kant, Darwin, Haeckel, or Marx, and sometimes almost came to fist fights over problems of Russian literature or modern art. When we graduated at the age of eighteen or nineteen we were well prepared for the university.

During my Gymnasium days I became interested in the East and since the language is the key to the understanding of every civilization I began learning Arabic. For a number of years I spent an early hour on the study of Arabic every morning before going to school. I then took the Hebrew courses that were offered at the Gymnasium to those students who intended to study theology. After graduation I registered in the Philosophical Faculty of the University of Zurich as a student of oriental philology. I continued my studies of Arabic and Hebrew and took up Sanskrit. And since the latter course proceeded rather slowly I worked with a private tutor and at the end of the year we were reading the Panchatantra and similar texts.

In those days the University of Zurich was rather weak in oriental studies and this determined me to spend most of the year 1911 in London. I had some excellent courses at University College, and since I was the only student attending them learned a great deal. With Mabel Bode I read the Meghaduta and with H. Hirschfeld the Fakhri and the Delectus Veterum Carminum Arabicorum of Noeldeke. At the same time I began the study of Chinese at King's College and devoted a great deal of time to it. My teachers were rather skeptical and repeatedly pointed out to me that it was impossible to embrace the whole Orient, that I would have to specialize either on the Near East, on India, or on the Far East. But I refused to specialize. I was interested in the East as a whole, in comparative religion and comparative literature, in the migration and transmission of literary subjects and similar problems. And since I was very young I thought that nothing would be impossible to me.

I worked very hard in those years and always had some grammar in my pocket and a notebook full of Chinese ideograms. But the time came when I had to admit that my teachers were right. It could not be done. The task became so big that even physically I could not master it. But I still refused to specialize and since I had always been greatly interested in science I went back to the University of Zurich and took the science courses that were given to students of science as well as to medical students.

There, again, it was my good fortune to have a great teacher, the professor of zoology and comparative anatomy, *Arnold Lang*. He was a former student of Haeckel, a great expert in zoology of the invertebrates and in genetics. His lectures were entrancing and we never missed a single one. During a course he never attempted to cover the whole field but discussed only a few selected subjects, a few animal forms, elements of genetics or similar topics. These he presented in great detail giving the history of the problem and discussing general principles connected with it. He could spend weeks developing the structure of one animal, drawing it in colored chalks on the blackboard. And when, at long last, he had given the finishing touch his bearded face brightened up and he felt like God after the creation of the world. He had recreated the worm, or the fish under our very eyes. And having watched this creative process we could never forget it. We had been allowed a glimpse into the work-shop of nature.

At the end of the course he apologized for having covered so little ground but added that we could easily find the rest in books, and that if we had followed him we would be able to consult and use books intelligently. I never had an opportunity to talk to Professor Lang. He did not know of my existence. I was just one of hundreds of students who crowded his lecture hall. But I was tremendously influenced by him because I had the privilege of watching the working of his mind. And from him I learned how to teach. Much later, when I became an academic teacher myself, I remembered how he had presented his subject, built up his lectures and organized his courses. The European university has a great tradition of academic oratory, an art that is not taught in courses but passed on from master to student through example and by the mere force of personality.

My year in science was a happy one and for a while I considered remaining in science, but again the phantom of specialization arose. What was it to be: chemistry or zoology or botany? Medicine seemed the broadest field, and so I became a medical student and never regretted it. Medicine undoubtedly is one of the most fascinating academic subjects in that it leads the student through heights and depths of human life.

I studied medicine at the University of Zurich where I graduated in 1917 and at the University of Munich where I spent the summer of 1914. I had many excellent teachers during the six years of my medical course but two of them stand out far above all others: *Friedrich von Müller* and *Ferdinand Sauerbruch*. They were very different but great teachers both.

Friedrich von Müller was at the height of his career when I took his course. He was professor of clinical medicine in Munich, a dignified gentleman and a great physician and scientist with vast cultural background. He represented the best type of German professor. His task was to introduce the young student into the field of clinical medicine. Every morning he gave a clinic of two hours at which he presented one typical case. Four students were called upon and with them he examined the patient and discussed the case, while the others watched them with breathless attention. His presentation invariably began with the question: "What do you see, what strikes you when you look at the patient?" whereby he meant to develop our faculty of observation. He repeated over and over again that medicine was not difficult provided we had a thorough foundation in anatomy, physiology and general pathology. "You must know the structure of the human body, its function and the mechanisms available to the organism to react against lesions. The rest boils down to observation and correct reasoning." And this was what we learned from him first of all: to observe phenomena and to reason correctly. I followed his precepts all through my studies and it saved me a lot of trouble. Von Müller's teaching was so impressive that to the present day I remember every individual case he presented during the course and even remember the face of many of the patients. The class-room was crowded with hundreds of students and a regular race for seats took place every morning.

Sauerbruch had an entirely different personality. He came from Marburg to Zurich in 1911 as professor of surgery. He was young, enthusiastic and temperamental. Students loved him or hated him but nobody who ever came in touch with him remained indifferent. He was an intuitive type of man, a brilliant surgeon who in his surgery as well as in his researches showed a great deal of imagination and originality. His clinic was inspiring and spectacular. Once, desiring to impress upon us the importance of the early operation of appendicitis, he demonstrated over twenty cases in one clinic, some of whom had been sent in for operation too late. Bed after bed was rolled in. The professor hardly said a word but the difference between the patients was striking. All those who had been operated on early looked flourishing while the others looked very sick. It was a piece of showmanship but nobody ever forgot the lesson. Sauerbruch taught us infinitely more than surgery. He made us think—think in terms of biology. A student could pass an examination with him without knowing many facts provided he was able to approach a case intelligently and to think properly. In his early years in Zurich Sauerbruch gave a course in general surgery that was attended by students of all classes, by the faculty and by the practitioners of the city. One had to be there an hour in advance to secure a seat. Every single lecture was a masterpiece, well-rounded, full of original ideas and challenging thoughts. It was certainly not by accident that Sauerbruch, like Müller and all great medical teachers I ever had, was deeply interested in the history of medicine and never missed an opportunity to make historical remarks. Men who made history were always aware of developments in which they were taking part. I was Sauerbruch's student for three years and came closer to him than to most of my medical teachers. He took a genuine interest in young people and kept an open house in which students were always welcomed.

I was an enthusiastic medical student, but remained interested in the humanities. In Zurich, medical school and university were on the same campus so that it was possible for medical students to attend courses in the academic division, which I frequently did. In Munich, once in the middle of the academic year I suddenly felt tired of the hospital and of medicine at large. I began skipping classes and spent the days in museums and art galleries, the night in theatres and concert halls. I was in a turmoil and when quite accidentally I met a friend in the street who was leaving the same day for Venice I decided to join him, and spent several weeks in Italy. For a while medicine was entirely forgotten and I lived in a world of history and art. Then, one evening, sitting in a café of the Piazza San Marco I felt an irresistible longing for the hospital, and there for the first time it occurred to me that medical history and the history of science might be a field in which I could combine all my interests. I went back to Munich the same night in a state of great elation. The next morning I resumed my hospital work with enthusiasm. In the afternoon I went to the Library where I found *Isis,* the journal recently launched by George Sarton, and the various publications of Karl Sudhoff. In the next few days I made a plan to study the various periods of the history of medicine and science by reading the most important texts. A German publisher was issuing a series of historical source-books that included the history of science and I soon was collecting materials for a history of oxidation. But then the war broke out. We were all called for practical work and the book was never finished.

Here I must recall one school that taught me perhaps just as much as the university, although I was not fully aware of it at the time: the Army. I served for nearly two years in the Medical Corps of the Swiss Army. In Switzerland every citizen is trained to be a soldier and medical students are automatically enlisted in the Medical Corps at the age of twenty, where they are promoted to higher rank according to their professional status and length of service. At the outbreak of the World War the entire army was mobilized and kept under arms for the first eight months. After that time when it became apparent that the country was not immediately threatened only one-half of the army was kept at the borders so that throughout the war we medical men spent half of the year in army service while we could continue our civilian work during the other half.

The two years in the army were a valuable experience to me in many respects. Medically I learned a great deal. We were often stationed in far remote mountain valleys where we had to attend the civilian population as well as the troops, sometimes under very difficult conditions. Much of the work was practical public health work in which I became greatly interested. The Medical Officers' Training School gave excellent instruction not only in war surgery but particularly in public health. In 1918 I had the good luck of being one of the first in my division to be stricken with influenza so that I was fit again when many of my fellow medical officers were sick. I spent most of the year treating influenza patients in a variety of troops and regions and worked for several months in the Influenza Bureau of the Surgeon General's office from which I was sent out to make epidemiological surveys all over the country.

But the army was a great school to me in other respects as well. So far I had lived the life of the middle class and had moved mostly in academic circles. I was interested in social problems but looked at them more from the theoretical and public health angle. In the army I came in close touch with the working class. In the cavalry to which I was attached for over a year the soldiers were peasants, in the artillery to which I was transferred later they were factory workers, most of whom were employed in several large metallurgical plants in the vicinity of Zurich. These anonymous soldiers became my teachers. They opened my eyes about many problems that I had not seen before and made me realize how little I knew about the world in which I was living. They made me visualize a field of research and activity equally important to the historian as to the medical man. They had confidence in me and on many evenings I went to the sickroom under the pretext of a late ward-round, sat on a bed and listened.

They discussed their own problems and discussed the war. And it often struck me how much more convincing their interpretations were than those I heard in the officers' mess. Switzerland, neutral but surrounded by warfaring countries, was an ideal post from which to observe events. Information was obtainable from all sides and it was much easier to get at the truth than in those countries where unilateral heavy propaganda obstructed the vision. The imperialistic character of the war soon became apparent and it was not difficult to realize the full significance of the Russian Revolution.

The armistice was signed and the war was over, at least nominally. I was twenty-seven years old. I had an all-round medical training and had acquired some practical experience in medicine and public health. During the interval between two service periods I had interned for a while in obstetrics and in my senior medical year I had done experimental research in the Pharmacological Institute of the University of Zurich under Prof. Cloetta, as the result of which I had published my inaugural dissertation under the title "Experimental investigations on the effect of chronic camphor medication on the normal and sick heart." And now the question arose what the next step would be.

I knew what I wanted and felt no hesitation about it. My field of research was to be medical history. To most of my former professors I was a lost sheep. "Medical history," they said, "is a delightful hobby for retired practitioners but there is no career in it." I was no longer a child and knew better. And this time I was right. In all my previous studies I had felt the need for an historical approach to any given problem. I saw that general history must by necessity remain fragmentary and lead to wrong interpretations if it does not include the history of science. And I felt, although rather vaguely at the time, that medical history studied in a broader sense could be developed into a method that could contribute to the solution of urgent social problems of medicine. In medical history I found a field that was not a narrow specialty and in which I could combine my various interests. I was fully aware that I was not yet equipped for such studies and that I would have to go back to school for at least three years. And since I could no longer afford to make a wrong start I went to Leipzig in 1919 as soon as conditions permitted in order to consult and work with *Karl Sudhoff*.

The Institute of the History of Medicine founded in 1905 at the University of Leipzig was at that time the undisputed centre of research in medical history. The Institute was Karl Sudhoff. He filled it with his powerful personality. It was his workshop that he had built up. He had no associates and no secretary and was only aided by an "Institutsdiener" who served him devotedly and kept the place in order. But he had a large group of students who wrote their inaugural dissertations under his guidance and published for him the texts in which he was interested. And every researcher in medical history from all over the world came to Leipzig to consult him and to use the resources of the Institute.

He was an indefatigable worker. From 1905 on, when he abandoned general practice and accepted the chair in Leipzig he published a large number of monographs, hundreds of papers and edited half a dozen journals and serial publications. His bibliography shows that in certain years he published over forty papers—mostly mediaeval medical texts that he had discovered in his annual peregrinations. He was a poor lecturer, was restless in his thinking so that he would jump abruptly from one subject to another without finishing his sentences. The lectures, therefore, were rather confused and it was hard to follow him. He exerted his tremendous influence not through teaching but through his writings and personal contacts. He had a kindly nature and could be very jovial, but he could also flare up and in such moments he looked like *Jupiter tonans*. His eyes sparkled and his voice was thunder. A dominating and domineering personality he could not tolerate to have anybody beside him, and colleagues who did not accept his leadership were excommunicated pitilessly.

He was different to me. He was infinitely more than a teacher, was like a father to me. My first visit in 1919 was the beginning of a very close association that lasted for many years. From 1919 to 1925 whether in Leipzig or in Zurich, I was in constant touch with Sudhoff. He supplied me with books, photostats and photographs from the Institute collections and helped me in any possible way. I had the privilege to assist him in reading and correcting galley proofs of several of his books, and we met every year at the annual meetings of the German Society of the History of Science, Medicine and Technology. From 1925 when I succeeded him in the chair at Leipzig to 1932 when I left for America, we met almost daily and there was not a thing on earth that we did not discuss. In 1933 I was awarded the Karl Sudhoff Medal and on the occasion he wrote in longhand an appreciation of my work that I treasure more than anything else. After that time to my deep sorrow our close relationship gradually came to an end. Karl Sudhoff had joined the National Socialist Party. It was a profound shock to me and for a long time I could not understand how he, a staunch liberal and rationalist all his life, could at the age of eighty become a Nazi and identify himself with Hitler's doings. I have only one explanation for it, that he was driven by his fanatic patriotism. He deeply felt and resented the humiliation of Germany after Versailles, and like so many others must have honestly believed that Hitler would be the saviour of his country.

Karl Sudhoff died in 1938. He was the great pioneer in medical history who not only advanced the subject by leaps and bounds through his researches but also organized it and gave it a definite place in the medical curriculum. The Leipzig Institute was the first research institute ever established in the field. It set a high standard of scholarship and served as an example that was soon to be followed by other universities in Germany and abroad. It was my good fortune that I could begin my career in such an institute and with such a teacher. It gave me a solid philological foundation without which serious studies are just as impossible in medical history as in any other historical discipline.

In 1921 at the age of thirty I felt sufficiently prepared to apply for an academic position. I was appointed *Privatdozent* at the University of Zurich where I had a small but devoted group of students. When Sudhoff retired in 1925 his chair and the directorship of the Leipzig Institute were offered to me. It was not an easy job to be the successor of such a great man. I realized that the task was not to imitate my predecessor but to preserve the high standard of the Institute while developing it along my own lines. Sudhoff was primarily interested in the philological side of medical history, in texts and documents that he published by the hundreds. I had become increasingly interested in the sociological approach to history and in the sociology of medicine. I saw that the application of medical knowledge to society was made so difficult by a variety of social, economic, political, religious and philosophic factors that had to be investigated if progress was to be achieved. Without neglecting philological studies I endeavored to develop the Institute more and more along the sociological line. My book *Man and Medicine* written in those years reflects this attitude.

It was in 1927 that I first came in touch with *William H. Welch*. He had done more for the development of scientific medicine in America than anybody else, and now nearing the end of his career he intended to establish at the Johns Hopkins University in Baltimore, with which he had been connected since 1884, an Institute of the History of Medicine similar to that in Leipzig. He was travelling in Europe purchasing books for the new Institute and came to Leipzig to discuss his plans with Karl Sudhoff. I was in touch with Dr. Welch from 1927 to the time of his death in 1934 and although I cannot claim him as one of my teachers I learned a great deal from him as everybody did who had the good fortune to be close to him. As a matter of fact, I wish I had learned more from him, particularly his inaggressive way of attaining an end by diplomatic means. Temperaments, however, are different.

The Johns Hopkins Institute was opened in 1929. Sudhoff went to America for the occasion. Two years later in 1931 I was invited as visiting lecturer. I spent two months at the Institute whereupon I went on a long lecture tour through all sections of the United States. And while I was travelling I was offered Dr. Welch's chair.

I was tremendously impressed by the United States. I found democratic institutions dear to me and found the country utterly different from what it is usually pictured by European travellers who see only the façade and the material aspect of American life. I was particularly impressed by the universities, by their earnest desire to raise standards of scholarship and to carry on the torch of learning. I found them fully aware of their great responsibility at a time when European institutions were breaking down under political and financial pressure. Great interest was shown all over the country in medical history, the importance of which had been emphasized by all medical leaders. And I found urgent social problems of medicine, eagerly discussed by all groups involved. The Committee on the Costs of Medical Care was at the peak of its activities. What appealed to me particularly was the dynamism of America and its brave experimental spirit, so utterly different from the stifling self-satisfaction and fossilizing feeling of superiority so often met with in Europe.

In Germany things were developing from bad to worse and it was apparent that the days of academic freedom were counted. It was not difficult, therefore, to come to a decision. Once more I was successor to a great man, in one of the world's great medical schools, in a university justly famous for its scholarship and liberal spirit. I was in charge of a young Institute, in a young and vast country— and I have enjoyed working in America ever since I first landed in the new world.

Ladies and Gentlemen,

I apologize for this lengthy personal history in an address devoted to the subject of university education. But instead of discussing the topic in a purely theoretical way I preferred to give you a practical demonstration in evoking the figure of some men who were great academic teachers and in discussing factors that contribute to the success of university education. Let me add a few remarks.

When I look back at my early university life it occurs to me that such a career would be rather difficult in America as well as in South Africa. Our students are so well protected, are guided and advised so well that they have hardly a chance to make mistakes. Much thinking is done for them, and they hardly have an opportunity to find things out for themselves. I made endless mistakes but I learned through them and found my own way.

I have a particular grudge against textbooks, the only literature ever consulted by many students. Instead of reading Plato or Newton the student reads about them and thinks that he knows them if he is able to repeat a few judgments read in a book. The textbooks present a subject carefully digested and in a simplified way. They read without effort and are forgotten overnight. Do not misunderstand me. There are excellent textbooks and when used judiciously they have an important function to fulfill. They allow a rapid orientation over a wide field. But they can never replace the study of original texts.

When a publisher wishes to recommend a book he advertises it as being "highly readable." He may even add that it is written in a "delightfully informal way." And when a reviewer wants to praise a book very highly he emphasizes its readability, by which he means that every fool can read it without effort. And yet we all know that the books that contribute most to the formation of our minds, the books that have made history, are anything but "highly readable." They are books with which we struggle, that we read and reread with pencil in hand, books that we have to conquer page by page. But once we have conquered them we possess them. Many subjects are difficult by nature and a presentation ceases to be true when it is over-simplified. No knowledge can be obtained without labor and we should not be afraid to require great efforts from our students.

The gown that we are wearing to-night is a mediaeval costume, and this reminds us that the Western university has a long tradition and a great past. From the mediaeval university we have inherited many external forms such as the organization in faculties, examinations, degrees and also the main forms of teaching: *lectio* and *disputatio*.

In the lectio the mediaeval professor read and interpreted a book, and the students wrote down what they heard. Books were rare and expensive in those days and the books the students wrote during the courses became the main body of their libraries. Conditions have changed since then. Printing has made books easily available and has reduced their price considerably. The function of the lecture, therefore, no longer is to dictate books. The student can buy them for little money. The lecture must give what the student will not so easily find in books, namely the living personal contact between man and man. In the lecture the professor, an expert in his field, thinks aloud and develops his own views on a subject. He has an ideal opportunity to stimulate the student, to arouse his curiosity or to challenge him, in other words: to make him think.

We can study a symphony at home, from the score and phonograph records, but this does not make concerts superfluous. In a concert we hear the interpretation of a symphony by a definite conductor and there is that magnetic contact between orchestra and audience that is so hard to define. The concert, moreover, inspires us and stimulates us to study music of which we had not thought before.

As a student I had a simple method which I found very helpful. When I knew what the subject of a lecture or a clinic would be I read about it before so as to have a certain preparation. During the lecture I made a few notes, as few as possible, just enough to be able to reconstruct the lecture. Students who write much do not listen. And then in the evening I consulted a number of books on the subject and wrote a summary of what I had read and heard, made notes about my personal impressions and doubts, and marked points that would require further study. I did it on loose leaves so as to be able to add to it on later occasions.

In the mediaeval *disputatio* professor and students discussed a subject, weighing the pros and cons of an argument. The corresponding modern form of teaching is the seminary course that was so strongly developed by the German university. Here the students take an active part, presenting papers, reporting on studies made, and the professor's function is to lead the discussion. Here the professor has an opportunity to teach methods of research, to show the students how to approach a problem, how to get at facts and how to interpret them.

The rise of modern science called for new forms of academic instruction unknown to the mediaeval university: laboratory courses and clinical instruction at the bedside of patients. These new methods of teaching so highly successful in the natural sciences begin to be applied to the social sciences. Political science cannot be taught in the class-room alone. It requires field work in parliaments and government offices. Economics is a dead subject if the student has no opportunity to watch the process of production and distribution in mines, factories, farms, shops, railroad offices and the stock exchange. And if sociology is to be more than the philosophy of history it requires still more extensive field work. The best curriculum is one in which the various forms of instruction, lecture, seminary course and practical work are perfectly balanced.

The task of university education is not to transmit an established body of knowledge because there is no such thing. Science and the humanities evolve from day to day. If a student left the university with nothing more than the knowledge accepted in his year of graduation he would soon be hopelessly behind. The university must do infinitely more than teach facts and theories. It must help the student to develop his faculties, must train him to think independently and critically, so that he may form his own judgments. It must teach

[25]

him methods of study so as to enable him to keep pace with developments. It must open up horizons for him, lead him in attaining a correct sense of values, in developing his attitude toward life, in one word, his philosophy. The actual work must be done by the student himself. Nobody can do it for him. But the university helps him by giving him the privilege to live and work for a number of years in close touch with a group of men who have devoted their lives to the advancement of knowledge.

If academic instruction is to be fruitful it must be based upon research. Only men who have been actually engaged in research are competent to present a subject adequately. The student feels instinctively whether a professor is merely abstracting a textbook or whether he speaks with authority. We all have to teach subjects that we have not explored ourselves, but if we are researchers we are able to evaluate other people's results critically. I am well aware that it is often extremely difficult for a professor to continue his researches. Many are unduly burdened with teaching. The rapid development of our universities has created so many administrative tasks that time and energy of many departmental heads are entirely absorbed by them. And since the professors are experts they are called upon for advice by the state and other agencies. It is impossible to evade these tasks. Academic teachers should not live cloistered in their studies but keep in close touch with life, feeling the pulse of a society for which they are preparing young people. Departments must be administered. They are serving not only present needs but are building up collections and storing experience for the future. It is increasingly difficult to be professor and researcher at the same time, and a situation has arisen that way wreck the university if a solution is not found.

In spite of all difficulties the academic teacher must remain a researcher. It means incessant hard work, and many amenities of life must be sacrified. But the compensations are endless.

There is another point to which I would like to draw your attention. The mediaeval university was the *Universitas Litterarum*. It emphasized the universality and unity of learning. It is true that it also trained young people to be physicians and lawyers, but medicine and the law were part of the general philosophy of the time and therefore close to theology. And the students of medicine and law were first trained for many years in the Faculty of Arts. The goal of university education was to produce an all-round scholar, an ideal that was carefully preserved for centuries. The word *doctor* means *scholar,* a point that we sometimes forget. Conditions changed in the nineteenth century when the development of science led to increasing specialization. A deep split occurred between the humanities and the new science. Many universities today are merely conglomerations of professional schools with hardly any bond between them.

Specialization occurred by necessity. No man can possibly embrace the entire realm of knowledge. If science, medicine and technology have progressed so tremendously, it was largely due to the specialization in research. We need highly trained specialists. But we need more than specialists. If there is so much trouble in the world today and if it is so extremely difficult to make necessary adjustments it is to a certain extent due to the fact that many men in leading positions are nothing but narrow specialists whose general and political education has been utterly neglected.

We who have the privilege of living in a democracy have not only professional duties but also duties as citizens. We have responsibilities not only toward our families and the institutions in which we work but also toward the community and society at large. How can we expect a democratic state to function efficiently if those men who had the maximum of education, who were trained in universities are mere specialists unprepared for their civic duties, unwilling to assume responsibility and leaving the welfare of society in the care of politicians whose only qualification very often is that they like the game and find it profitable?

It seems to me that here the university has an extremely important function to fulfill. The point is not to set the clock back and to return to the Middle Ages. We shall continue to develop highly trained specialists, but we must give them a broader equipment. In South Africa as in England students enter professional colleges immediately after leaving secondary school, which greatly reduces the opportunities for general higher education. In the United States the requirements for admission to a professional school include either a completed or at least a few years' course in a College of Arts and Sciences. This is better but still not enough. General education must continue in the professional schools and must be correlated to the subject of the course. Whatever a man's specialty is going to be, he should be familiar with its history, its sociology, its philosophy. This will by necessity broaden his outlook and increase his usefulness.

We must try to overbridge the gap between the old humanities and the new science, between the social and the natural sciences. If the old humanities include studies in ancient science they will not die but remain eternally young, a source of inspiration and happiness for generations to come. If history includes the history of science it will become a still more powerful weapon in the shaping of the future. If economics and sociology get closer to the natural sciences and adopt more of their methods they will greatly benefit by it. And if we succeed in bringing the humanities and the social sciences into the natural sciences we shall be able to develop a scientist who will be more than a narrow specialist, who will be aware of the place of science in the world and of its function in society. Nothing could be more encouraging than to see that already there are great scientists, great specialists in their respective fields, men like J. B. S. Haldane, J. Needham, H. Levy in England, J. Langevin in France who without neglecting their laboratories, are fully conscious of the burning problems of our time and are taking an active part in their solution.

My own work as an academic teacher is devoted to the task of preparing physicians who will be aware of the historical moment in which they live, aware of their great social responsibilities and of the economic necessities of medicine so that they will be equipped to take an active and intelligent part in the life of society and in the developing of a system of medical services that will reach everybody, whether rich or poor, whether white or black.

Ladies and Gentlemen,

Once more I wish to express my profound gratitude for the great honor bestowed upon me by this University. I appreciate it more than I can tell, not only because it shows me that you did not regret having invited me to South Africa as a visiting lecturer, but because it connects me permanently with a University for which I have a great admiration and to which I have become deeply attached.

It was my privilege to meet many members of your faculty and many of your students, and I was greatly impressed by their progressive attitude and liberal outlook. I have no doubt that the young men and women trained in this University will exert a marked influence upon the destinies of the country.

I shall be proud to wear your colors in America and I want you to consider me an American outpost of the University who will always be happy to serve you.

And so let me end by saying: Long live, grow and flourish *our* University—the University of the Witwatersrand.

3
War and Culture

THE WAR is in its third year. It has spread to one country after another and has truly become a world war. If ever a thesis has been proven correct, it was that of the indivisibility of peace. Millions of people, men, women and children, have already died and many more millions are doomed. Millions of families have been driven from their homes. A migration of nations, such as history has never seen before, is going on. The lights have gone out. Will it be total darkness? Will the world revert to barbarism?

First, we should remember that if the lights went out, it did not happen in 1939. The 21 years between the two world wars were anything but years of light. From the moment the treaty of Versailles was signed, the world knew that it must expect a series of new wars. They came soon enough. From 1931 on, one country after another was invaded by aggressive nations with the tacit consent of the great powers. The world, after it had recovered from the immediate effects of the last war, went through a period of economic boom with all its disgusting symptoms when people believed that they could advance themselves in the world by gambling instead of by performing honest hard work. Then came the crash of 1929, ten years of economic stagnation, with millions of people deprived of work and suffering mental and physical misery, in the midst of plenty, in sight of the idle tools they could have handled so well.

The lights went out, not in 1939, but around 1911 when the process of which the present war is but an episode entered into its critical stage. We have had a thirty-years' war already.

The purpose of this article, however, is not to discuss the causes of the war. There is another point that I have much at heart, the preservation of culture.

War and culture do not go together. War is always a reversal to primitive savagery. Whenever a war breaks out, it signifies that civilization has collapsed somewhere. It shows that the civilized methods of solving a problem—international cooperation, scientific

Written in 1941.

planning, negotiation and arbitration—have failed and that there seemed nothing else left but to settle the argument—for the moment—in the primitive way, with the fists. Nobody can kill fellow men with impunity. Of course we know that killing in self defense is legitimate and that many noble actions, deeds of great heroism, are performed in war. When a country is attacked by a ruthless enemy, it has only the choice between fighting back or accepting ignoble servitude. We atone for the killing by being willing to sacrifice our own life. We know, nevertheless, that blood always leaves stains, and that no one kills without suffering for it. War is always savage and the negation of culture.

War is destructive. It destroys not only human lives but also historical records that constituted the memory of nations, works of art that were sources of inspiration to generations. The world will be greatly impoverished in its cultural heritage after this war, although the actual loss may not be as great as we would expect because the war was so easy to foresee. At a time when statesmen were too stupid or too cowardly to prepare for war, librarians and directors of museums showed more wisdom and courage and did get ready.

War destroys endless numbers of actual and potential material values that could have been used for cultural purposes. Uncounted millions of hours of labor are spent to produce the instruments of destruction. On armistice day highly specialized machinery, wonders of technology, worth billions of dollars, will all of a sudden turn into mere scrap iron. A fraction of that money would have been enough to provide the means for eradicating a number of diseases. When in the summer of 1941 two battleships were sunk within a few days, the *Hood* and the *Bismarck,* values went to the bottom of the sea that would have been sufficient to equip and maintain two universities.

War always tends to lower the cultural standard of the people involved. In wartime the armed forces automatically become the most important section of society. As a result of hardship, enforced celibacy and the constant proximity of death, the soldier's most urgent want becomes the satisfaction of animal instincts. The rest of the population, whose main function becomes that of supplying the armed forces with all they require, is obviously affected by this attitude.

And yet culture is needed in wartime more than ever. Why? War is not an end in itself; only the perverted ideology of fascism could

[31]

declare war the normal condition of mankind and peace the mere interval between two wars. War is to society what an acute disease is to the individual, a deep crisis in the course of its life. Whether it results in recovery or death depends to a large extent on the cultural forces that a country possesses. France was thoroughly defeated in 1871, and yet the country recovered in an incredibly short time. It did so because Claude Bernard was still alive, because Berthelot and Pasteur were at the height of their careers, because the country had scholars like Renan and Taine, writers like Flaubert and Zola, composers like Saint-Saëns and César Franck, because the impressionist school was just bursting forth. Where such powerful creative forces are at work a country cannot be defeated. It took Germany with her *Gründerjahre* much more time to recover from her victory.

In 1918 Germany had collapsed and yet there were strong symptoms of recovery. The young students who returned from the war threw themselves body and soul into the most abstract studies. Science flourished with men like Einstein, Meyerhof, Warburg. In the universities, the departments of classics, Sanskrit and Chinese were crowded as never before. New chairs were created every day. When finances were at a very low ebb, the Prussian government spent one million marks for the purchase of an archaic Greek statue of incredible beauty. It justly felt that this was one of the best investments a defeated nation could make. The country approved of the purchase, and the statue became a source of inspiration and happiness to innumerable people. If Germany did not recover, but developed into a malignant power that threatened the world with destruction, it was partly attributable to the fact that the war did not actually end in 1918 but was continued with different means.

Today wars are fought on such a tremendous scale that every party, victor and victim, is bound to suffer. Every party's economy is shattered after the war, and every one must face a tremendous task of reconstruction. Such a task cannot be fulfilled unless a country has preserved its cultural resources intact, and the greatest mistake we could make in the present emergency would be to neglect our institutions of culture.

Of all branches of learning, the sciences will probably suffer least. Modern warfare has become so highly technical that it requires the mobilization of all scientific resources that a country possesses. Every day presents new problems, and the war undoubtedly will accelerate the development of many branches of science. Of many, but not of all. War science is necessarily one-sided. It is primarily technical and calls for the engineer, the physicist and chemist. After the war, however, we shall be in dire need of a universal science. The task will be infinitely greater than at the present moment, when we shall have to use all the scientific knowledge we possess for the reconstruction of the world, when we shall have to apply scientific principles to the basic processes of social life, production, distribution and consumption. This is why right now we must not neglect but, on the contrary, must develop such seemingly unnecessary fields as genetics, theoretical biology, history, sociology and philosophy of science.

To medicine every war is a challenge. The armed conflict creates an emergency which calls for large numbers of personnel and presents many new problems. The number of physicians needed per capita of the armed forces is much larger than that normally required for the population. No country has a reserve of medical personnel. Hence there is bound to be a shortage of physicians in the civilian population. This is particularly serious in modern wars which are fought not between armies alone but between nations. The shortage must be compensated by improved organization that will eliminate every source of waste and inefficiency. Thus war becomes a testing ground for a nation's ability to organize all its health services, and it may become a rich source of experience for the organization of services after the war.

I think we are all aware that when this war is over, the world will be different from what it was before. There will be no return to the happy-go-lucky methods of the past. Even in times of great prosperity we were unable to provide all medical services to all the people who needed them. The organization of medical care will be imperative after the war, and we must do the planning now.

The medicine and surgery practised on battlefields are obviously not always of the highest quality because of the pressure of the emergency. The preservation of standards requires that medical research and teaching institutions be kept intact and functioning as much as ever possible. A research institution is a very delicate organism. The disruption of teams of researchers hampers its efficiency and thus harms the nation.

We must intensify our studies not only in the basic sciences, in clinical medicine and public health, but also in view of the post-war problems in the sociology and economics of medicine.

The necessity of not neglecting the social sciences is obvious. History is one of the most powerful driving forces of life. Every situation that we come to face, every problem that we are called upon to solve, are the results of historical developments and trends. The way we act is largely determined by the picture we have of our past. Without sound knowledge of history we can act instinctively and opportunistically, but we cannot act intelligently. The present conflict is the climax of historical developments of which the origins reach far back, and we cannot understand it unless we are aware of these processes. History does repeat itself. Germany again overran France following the old plan of von Schlieffen. Russia is defeating Germany very much along the lines of Kutusov's tactics and at Pearl Harbor an attempt was made to revive the old method of "Copenhaguing" a fleet. The reconstruction of the world after the war will call for a mobilization of all resources of historical scholarship we possess, and it is therefore extremely important that the work that is going on at the moment be not interrupted. Studies that may seem far remote from the present problems may all of a sudden become of very acute interest.

What has been said of history applies also to other social sciences such as economics, sociology, anthropology and geography. We must admit that the present war is not merely a struggle for markets, but that deep social and economic issues are involved. The world has changed in the last hundred years. We live in a highly industrialized, highly technical and specialized society that calls for solidarity. We depend on each other for our welfare more than ever. After two centuries of enlightenment the day will come when the people will refuse to produce anarchically, in fits, following the whims of a stock market, in periods of boom and depression. They will call for the scientist to replace the gambler and will refuse to accept economic crises as natural catastrophes. They have assumed the duty to work, but they will claim the right to work. Hitler would never have obtained a following if he had not succeeded in giving his people an amount of social security for which they were willing to sacrifice their liberties.

Whether we like these developments or not makes no difference.

They exist; and the step from the competitive to the cooperative society will be taken. We can oppose developments and prolong throughout the century the period of wars that began around 1911. But we can also courageously face the situation in which we find ourselves, make the necessary adjustments in a democratic way, and thus shorten the period of wars.

Since the world has become very small, solidarity is needed not only among the citizens of one commonwealth but among nations. We may succeed in having a high standard of living in this country, but if our neighbors of Mexico or Japan live on a low standard we can be sure that this will affect us and cause trouble for us. Not only war and peace but also misery and prosperity are indivisible. The time is gone when one country could prosper at the expense of another. Nations are seeking not only political but economic independence, and the colonial problem will require thorough revision. Trusteeship over the still undeveloped races must become one in fact and not only in name.

Poverty still is the curse of mankind. Wherever we attack a problem, in every country, we encounter this seemingly unsurmountable barrier. It can be overcome. We already possess the technology that permits us to do this, and science is giving us new weapons every day. What we need are adjustments in the social organization.

The social scientists are facing a task of tremendous magnitude, a task that requires not only knowledge but imagination and courage. Their work is needed more than ever if we wish to win not only the war but the peace as well.

To the law every war is a serious test. Attempts to legalize war and to have it follow rules have failed with few exceptions. When a nation is fighting for its existence, every means seems right. War is international anarchy, a reversal to the law of the jungle. War is terribly confusing to the people's sense of right and wrong and to their sense of justice. Actions that are considered criminal under normal conditions are glorified when performed on the enemy. In war guilty and innocent suffer alike, and many more innocent than guilty. War hysteria may develop under certain circumstances and lead to a distortion of the law. This has happened more than once in history. Yet the law is the most important cultural institution of a nation, its very backbone. In a great emergency, in self defense, a nation has to curtail rights, must impose duties and must sometimes apply methods that it would never use in normal times. Great care must be taken, however, that the basic rights remain untouched. The justice of a cause suffers irreparable damage if the people lose confidence in the general administration of justice.

The cultural fields most likely to suffer from the war are the humanities and the arts. To the superficial observer they may seem a luxury that a country cannot afford in times of emergency. Nothing could be more wrong. Studies in the humanities are like those in "pure science" which are pursued for their own sake without any regard for practical applicability. And yet many such studies have led to great practical results. In the same way, studies of pure scholarship may prove to be of great practical value. England, France, Germany and Italy developed strong schools of Oriental Languages. They were centers of research investigating the languages, literature, history and institutions of the countries of the East. They also served for the preparation of consular officials, missionaries and other persons who intended to live and work in the Orient. We have neglected developing such a school, and yet there is no doubt that at the present moment it would render invaluable services.

A great country like the United States with extended international relations never knows when it will need expert information on Eastern European, Asiatic or African affairs. If such information is to be accurate, it must be based on scholarly research. Research institutions, however, cannot be improvised. It takes years for them to mature.

It would be perfectly stupid to neglect German, Italian or French studies because we dislike the present rulers of these nations. The great cultural values with which they have enriched the world so lavishly are timeless and will continue to exert their creative power when the memory of the present rulers will be a mere shadow. Quite apart from the cultural value of such studies, they have right now tremendous practical importance. Sooner or later we shall sit at the conference table with the delegates from these nations, and we shall face the task of rebuilding the world together. The more we know of each other, the more intelligently we shall be able to act. We shall need information, not only about their geography and economic conditions, but also about their psychology as it reveals itself in their literature which becomes accessible only through the language. I think we are now paying a high price for having neglected a more careful study of Germany. If we had learned from past mistakes, we would now crowd the German departments of our universities.

As was said before, war is to a society what a serious illness is to an individual. It suddenly interrupts the normal rhythm of our life, suddenly breaks in upon our daily routine. The proximity of death sets the mind in motion. We suddenly see problems that we never had the time to consider. Accepted values are re-evaluated. Has our life been what we wanted it to be? Have we been true to our principles? If we have failed, what can we learn from our failures and how shall we live in the future? A serious illness has been the turning point in many an individual's life.

In a similar way, war interrupts the normal life of a nation. The sudden emergency that breaks in like a natural catastrophe threatening destruction calls for a careful and sincere analysis of the nation's past and present, and for a re-affirmation of principles. Has it lived up to its great traditions? Has it merely paid lip-service to them or has it progressed in a creative way approaching and solving new problems in the spirit of its traditions? Is it prepared for the future, not only for the war but for the world that will follow it?

Paradoxical as it sounds, the most powerful makers of history are not the statesmen nor the generals, but the philosophers. There would be no United States without the philosophers of the period of enlightenment. Napoleon's power was due not so much to his military genius as to the fact that he represented the ideas of the French Revolution. Karl Marx wrote a book in the library of the British Museum and the result was the Soviet Union. The philosopher is a product of his time, to be sure, of the society of which he is a member. He is not a specialist, but using the results of specialists he studies the world in its entirety and is able to formulate the views and aspirations of the people. What millions of people only vaguely feel, he can express in words and put into a system. Once formulated, a philosophy becomes a powerful driving force. The most formidable weapon the United States possesses in this war is not its Navy, not its Air Force or Army, but its Declaration of Independence and Bill of Rights.

The philosopher is the nation's intellect. He thinks and is able to formulate thoughts. The voice of the people that expresses its emotions, its joys and sorrows, its hopes and fears, its anxieties and elation, is the artist. The writer, the poet, the painter, the sculptor, the composer, they all hold a very important place in society that becomes still more important in times of stress and strain. In such times they must live still closer to the people, working and feeling with them. They have the gift of expression. Their voice, their works liberate, stir, elate, or express the anguish that many feel. Deep as an emotion or an experience may be, it passes and is soon forgotten unless it has found artistic expression.

A good test for the justice of a cause and for the creative forces it possesses is to be found in the artistic manifestations it produces. The Spanish war was a good example. The Loyalists fought against a coalition of fascist and fascistically inclined powers for political and social justice, for the liberation of the people from the bonds of poverty, disease, ignorance and superstition. They gave their blood to build a better world for their children. Illiterate soldiers learned to read and write in the trenches between two battles. Schools and nurseries were built while the country was fighting for its very existence. There is no wonder that on the Loyalist side there was an outburst of poetry while nothing came from the fascist side that was fighting for the preservation of a rotten status quo. I do not know any more stirring and moving document than the *Romancero General de la Guerra de España*. The fascists could execute tens of thousands of people, but they will never be able to kill these verses and songs. They live in the hearts of the people. With these songs on their lips the people of Spain will rise again and this time will succeed in liberating their country.

The preservation of culture and of all cultural activities in a period of national emergency is a task the importance of which cannot be estimated highly enough. Our schools, libraries, museums, conservatories, theaters and studios are arsenals too, and the people working in them are soldiers also, fighting for the common cause. The cost of maintaining cultural institutions is infinitesimal compared with the costs of actual warfare. The benefits derived from them are endless and the attempt to curtail funds for cultural activities would be suicide.

Mere maintenance of what we possess, however, is not enough. In times like these, history moves very fast. Stagnation means retrogression. We must advance to keep abreast of the march of history. And this requires honest, courageous self-criticism.

Today the issue is clear. We want to defeat not only German, Italian and Japanese imperialisms because they happen to clash with our own economic interests; we also want to defeat fascism. We do not want to be ruled by a political philosophy that denies equal rights to all men and women, to all races and creeds; by a philosophy that denies the fact that the people are able to govern themselves. We also want leaders but not sultans. We refuse to live in a world of fear and apprehension, and we cherish the basic rights that the American Constitution guarantees because we are willing to accept the duties they imply.

We must be aware, however, that there is fascism not only in Germany, Italy, Japan and their satellites, but that conditions which lead to fascism exist in every country. Fascism must be exterminated not only on foreign battlefields but on the home front as well. If we abhor Hitler's racial policy, we must not apply it at home. No institution that discriminates against fellow-citizens on account of their race, creed, or sex has a right to use the word democracy. If we abhor Hitler's labor policy, we must give labor its rights. If we are truly convinced that our form of government is the best—and I for one am convinced that democracy is the only form of government worthy of man—we must stop being afraid of having the government assume increasing responsibilities. We must stop being lenient toward graft, corruption and inefficiency and must consider them as they really are, namely, treason, a betrayal of democracy. Democracy is challenged today. It can and will survive, but this will require not only that we win the war but that we have the intelligence to make the necessary social and economic adjustments.

We abhor Hitler's regimentation of all cultural activities. The researcher and the artist feel free in this country. Nobody prescribes what they have to do. But are they truly free? Is there not a regimentation of a more subtle kind, by the exigencies of the market? Can the poet or the painter make a living if he does not conform with the taste of the propertied class? In other words, have we created the conditions for culture, in city and country? Are we paying adequate salaries to our teachers and researchers?

Every great crisis that interrupts the routine of our life calls for self-examination. If we do not evade the issues but approach them sincerely and courageously, we shall emerge from this great crisis stronger, not only economically, but also culturally.

We are told that eighteen workers are needed in the rear to supply one man in the fighting line. I think that more than eighteen are needed. Needed are also the researcher, the scientist and the scholar, the teacher, the poet and the artist, all the cultural workers. Their labor will determine to a large extent whether the soldier's victory will be lost, or whether it shall become a gain to the nation and the beginning of a better world.

4

On the Threshold of Another Year of War

WE HAVE just had a significant experience at the Johns Hopkins Institute of the History of Medicine. On June 1, 1942 our School of Medicine, like the other schools of the country, opened the new academic year on the accelerated program. The students are trained in three instead of four calendar years. The summer vacation is cut down to four weeks and the students are given in three years the same number of courses and hours that they used to receive in four. They have in addition courses in first aid, war medicine and similar subjects. This obviously is a measure of emergency because medical education does not consist of courses and hours alone. It also requires reading and thinking and experience gained during the vacations. It is a slow process of digesting and assimilating the materials presented, of developing the faculties of observation and reasoning, of growing into the subject and maturing in it. Four calendar years, even if well used, are hardly long enough. But the country needs many doctors and needs them quickly so that there could be no hesitation: the accelerated program was imperative and could be accelerated still more if circumstances should call for it.

Since all courses of the Institute of the History of Medicine are elective we did not expect any students at all this year. We assumed that under the circumstances they would not have the time, leisure or desire to attend courses that are not required. Consequently we planned only for a few research seminars intended primarily for the members of the staff, in addition to a general introductory lecture course.

Just the contrary happened: we had this year more students than ever before in the history of the Institute. The lecture course given by one of my associates (16 hours) was crowded and the students held out to the last day in spite of the Baltimore summer heat. All other courses were unusually well attended. To my Seminar in the Sociology of Medicine (4 months, 2 hours a week from 8-10 p. m.), as a rule, I admit only 12 or 15 advanced students with whom I

Written in 1942.

[41]

investigate some aspect of the problem. This year the demand for admission, particularly from members of the first-year class, was such that I had to throw the Seminar open and had to change its whole plan.

Four medical students asked one of my associates to give them a course in the philosophy of Plato, one hour a week throughout the year. My associate answered that he would be glad to read the Timaeus with them and to discuss Plato's views on science, but the students made clear that it was not Plato's science but his philosophy at large that they intended to study.

This had never happened to us before. It shows that our young students have been stirred up tremendously by the war. They feel that they are in the midst of a gigantic historical process that will affect their lives deeply, about the nature of which, however, they are not quite certain. They also feel vaguely that medical practice after the war will be different for most of them than it had been in the past and they want to know why. They are being trained to serve their country as physicians in the armed forces and on the home front. Their spirit is splendid and they are ready for any sacrifice but they want to know what the issues are. They justly feel that the historical and sociological analysis can help them in clarifying their thought and they come to us with endless questions. If the university cannot help them, who else could?

I think that we academic teachers have a tremendous responsibility toward our students, now more than ever. We cannot tell them the Truth because we do not know it. We cannot predict the future for them because nobody can. But being older, having studied these problems for a longer time and perhaps more thoroughly, we may be able to help them in seeing and interpreting events, trends, and developments. The technical knowledge we give our students is important, of course, but just as important is the outlook and attitude we help them develop. Wars are not won by machines but by the spirit of the men who handle them. Stalingrad has been a lesson. It is wrong for a university to fold up in time of war and turn into a mere technical institute. It must impart technical knowledge and skills, to be sure, hurriedly and concentratedly, but we must do it in the academic way. It is the method that makes it, and the personality of the teacher. Philosophy can be taught without special courses, ın discussing the design of an airplane; instruction in sociology can be given while poison gases are being prepared. There is more philosophy, psychology and sociology involved in every clinical case that turns up in the hospital than the specialists could dream of. A university is a living community of teachers and students struggling together for knowledge and understanding. The subject of instruction may vary but the spirit is the same, and a country in which the universities lose that spirit finds itself greatly impoverished.

As professor of history in a medical school at this particular moment, I am doubly aware of my responsibility. In the next academic year I intend to give a course on *The Historical Foundations of the Present World Conflict* in which I will analyze the social, economic, political and medical developments that took place in the period that preceded the war. I am well aware that I will not be able to teach the students much. All I can do is think aloud for them and let them participate in my endeavor to understand the world in which I happen to live and in which I, as a member of a democratic society, am expected to play an intelligent part.

My next Seminar in the Sociology of Medicine I intend to devote to a study of *Social Security Legislation from Bismarck to Beveridge.* The report of Sir William Beveridge to the British Parliament on Social Insurance and Allied Services is by far the most interesting document that has come from the war so far. It is a challenge to every country and to every one of us. It raises basic issues that cannot be postponed until after the war but must be decided now because they well may determine the ultimate outcome of the war. It is not easy to interpret the full meaning of this Report. Is it a step toward the solution of our social problem or is it, as a prominent British conservative put it, merely "the cheapest insurance against revolution," an attempt to bribe the workers into complacency? Will such a plan stifle the people's initiative or will it, on the contrary, stimulate it?

The Beveridge plan does not represent a new departure but is merely the most recent step in a development that began in Germany in 1883. I feel unable to appreciate the Report without a thorough historical and sociological analysis. I want to know what the social, economic and political conditions were that made Bismarck launch a vast social security program in Germany in 1883, Lloyd George in England in 1911, the French government in 1928, and so many

[43]

other countries at a definite historical moment. What were the driving forces, the motives, the justifications, the inhibitions?

Thus, very selfishly, I will hold this Seminar primarily for my own enlightenment, but I think that it will also help the students to approach these issues more intelligently when they will become acute in this country.

*

What I have mentioned so far points to the fact that this war has a different character from other wars. It is not merely a clash between competing imperialisms. There are enough imperialistic elements involved, to be sure, but basically it is a revolutionary war, a gigantic war of liberation, of the oppressed nations and the oppressed groups within nations.

In the last war the delineation was clear: Germans were Germans, Italians Italians and Frenchmen Frenchmen. Today in 1942 the Germans are nazis and anti-nazis, the Italians are fascists and anti-fascists and the confusion is indescribable in France where a rotten bourgeoisie is destroying itself, while a heroic underground is preparing the regeneration of the country. In the Allied Nations there are many who wish for the preservation of the status quo, the very condition that led to the present catastrophe, while others want a new world to emerge on the ruins of the old. It would be a great mistake to consider this war an unpleasant interruption of our normal life. The world of tomorrow will by necessity be different from that of yesterday, and what we thought was our "normal life" will never come back again.

Wherever we look we find that in every field technology has outrun sociology. We have the scientific knowledge that would enable us to produce all the food that the inhabitants of the globe could possibly consume and yet there are still famines in the world, and it is no exaggeration to state that more than one-half of the population of the earth suffers from malnutrition. With the technical knowledge and skills we possess, we could produce all the commodities that people could possibly want to use, and yet the majority of mankind still lives in dire poverty. We have the medical knowledge needed to wipe out many diseases, but we still have them among us. We have built means of transportation that overbridge the continents, but not the apparatus that ensures peaceful cooperation between nations.

Science progressed more rapidly than social organization, and things were bound to come to a breaking point. We did nothing to prevent this war. We saw the forces of destruction arise and become stronger every day, but we closed our eyes and failed to see that once war started anywhere, it would by necessity spread like wildfire.

I think we should count with a long duration of the war if for no other reason than that it is global. A war that is affecting every country and in which such deep social and economic issues are involved cannot end suddenly. There will be armistices, to be sure, perhaps in a not too distant future, but from them to world peace there will still be a very long way. The German war machine may collapse some day as suddenly as it did in 1918, but the liquidation of nazism will take more time.

If the war is to last long, we must adjust ourselves to it as we adjusted ourselves to a long period of economic depression. We must make decisions now and not postpone them, because "after the war" may be many years from now and it may then be too late. We must not drop our cultural activities. In a total war they are a potential also and we may find it difficult to resume them later. Shostakovich's Seventh Symphony was a great Russian victory too. At a moment when we are cancelling all scientific conventions, the Russians, hard-pressed as they are, had time to hold large and impressive meetings in commemoration of the tercentenary of the birth of Isaac Newton, not only in Moscow but in Kazan, Sverdlovsk, Tashkent and other places. And the Chinese have demonstrated to the world how cultural activities must be carried on even under most devastating conditions.

Now that so many of us are in the armed forces, those of us who are left behind must work twice as hard as before, must give up every thought of comfort and readily accept living on a rapidly decreasing standard that will not rise so soon again. There will be many casualties on the home front too because the human heart can stand only a certain amount of stress, but the readiness to sacrifice one's life for a just cause is not a privilege of the young people alone.

*

[45]

While the destructive aspects of the war are obviously in the foreground, it nevertheless creates immediate opportunities that should not be neglected.

We have today one and a half million American troops in foreign lands with many more to follow, mostly young people who have never been abroad and would probably never have had a chance to see a foreign country. This obviously presents an educational opportunity such as we have never had before.

In Great Britain and Ireland many American soldiers will find the country of their ancestors. In New Zealand and Australia they will come in touch with some of the socially most advanced nations in the world. In China they will participate in the heroic struggle of a highly cultured people against foreign invasion and will witness the birthpains of a new China. In India they will see a country at a decisive moment of its history while it is striving for independence. North Africa will permit them a glimpse into the colorful world of Islam, and soon they may find themselves in Greece and Italy.

This contact with foreign countries cannot but be a stirring experience which must broaden their horizon. It will make them appreciate their home country the more and will also make them understand it the better. From all these foreign lands people came to America and the result of their cooperative efforts was the United States of today. The great benefit we derive from travelling abroad is not only that we come in touch with different people and institutions, but also that we learn to see our own country with different eyes.

The American soldier abroad will see how different people are in color, language, and customs but he will also find that they are basically the same everywhere sharing the same hopes and aspirations. He will perhaps conclude that there is no reason why under a proper social organization the different races of mankind should not live as peacefully together in the world as they do in the United States.

It is obvious that the soldiers abroad will need some help and guidance to understand and evaluate the seemingly strange worlds in which they find themselves transplanted, and I do not know whether the educational work is as well organized in the American army as it is in the British and in the Russian armies, but there can be no doubt that the opportunity is unique.

In civilian life it is left to the individual to find his place in society. He may find the job for which he is best fitted or he may not. The army, requiring maximum efficiency, must have the right man at the right place. Aptitude tests are being made on millions of people who then are assigned to the task for which they are best equipped. And if they do not possess the training required for the job, they are given it. The economic mechanism which under normal conditions makes a rational selection so difficult does not operate in the army which is basically a socialized community.

Thus many young men receive training, learn techniques and acquire knowledge and skills that they would not have had without the war. But more than this: the entire nation, military and civilian, men, women, adolescents, working under great strain, raise their qualification considerably. This is a great gain to the country, and we must see to it that it is not lost after the war and that the forces are fully utilized for the work of reconstruction.

To women, this war will be one more step toward their emancipation. The last war already improved their status but by no means enough. There was still much discrimination against them, when married teachers were dismissed, women workers were paid lower wages than men doing equal work, when women were refused internships in many hospitals or their admission to medical schools was limited arbitrarily, when facilities were refused to them that would permit them to be both workers and mothers. Even now we do not make full use of the woman power of the country, and magazines take great pains in picturing their part in the war effort in the musical comedy style which is an insult to their honest and serious endeavor.

The part of women, however, has already been so great, in the armed forces, civilian defense services, in the professions, in factory and farm, office and store, that it will be difficult after the war to deny them aptitudes which they have so plainly demonstrated to possess.

*

On the threshold of a new year of war, we expect relentless work and hardships for all, suffering and death for many. But with the certitude of ultimate victory we combine the hope that the sacrifices will not be in vain. We know that history moves slowly. We are impatient because the span of human life is so short. But as physicians, we know that there are the pains of death and the pains of birth, and we hope that the great suffering that the world is experiencing today will prove to be the end of all that was rotten and foul in our social organization and the beginning of a better world, with more justice and more responsibility, more freedom and more discipline, more happiness and more love.

5

Commemorating Andreas Vesalius

IN THE MIDST of one of the most devastating wars that kills soldiers and civilians alike and wipes out entire populations, it is encouraging to hear of the great achievements of military medicine. Every day medical journals and the press report of new life-saving treaments, and there is no doubt that the knowledge and skill of our physicians and surgeons are able to preserve an endless number of human lives that would have been lost only a few decades ago.

We are justly gratified by the great advance of medical science, by the progress achieved during the last fifty years, but at the same time we are aware that this is but the culminating point in a long development. Great achievements were possible because centuries of research preceded our time. And when we feel inclined to rejoice, we cannot but remember our ancestors, the men who did the pioneering work against tremendous odds. Our mind wanders to the Renaissance, to the year 1543 when Andreas Vesalius, a young man of twenty-eight years, published his immortal work, Seven Books on the Structure of the Human Body—*De humani corporis fabrica libri septem.*

The *Fabrica* represents one aspect of the discovery of the world that took place during the Renaissance. It is one expression of the trend toward realism characteristic of the period. People began to be tired of speculation and wanted to see things with their own eyes. But the book was more: it marked a turning point in the history of medicine, or rather, it was the starting point of a new medical science. During the Middle Ages eastern and western medicine had developed on the same foundations along similar lines, but only the West had the experience of the Renaissance and made anatomy the basis of a new medicine, while the East followed traditional lines to our day.

Upon the foundation of human anatomy a new anatomical physiology was built during the 17th century, a new anatomical pathology during the 18th century. The symptoms of disease appeared as the

Written in 1943.

[49]

functio laesa of anatomically changed organs. Clinical medicine was given a new and infinitely productive method of research. Observing the clinical course of diseases and writing case histories, performing autopsies on deceased patients and writing autopsy reports, the physicians of the 19th century by comparing the two documents were able to establish well defined disease entities that were not determined by their symptomatology alone but by the underlying anatomical lesion.

On the basis of this new approach the medical specialties developed. Instruments were devised that made the anatomy of the organs accessible to the physician's eye. And modern surgery was nothing else but the triumph of anatomical therapy.

Once the anatomical cycle was closed, medical science logically developed a functional, physiological approach, one however that remains based on anatomy. The development of chemistry and the discovery of pathogenic microorganisms opened up new horizons, and all these combined factors contributed to the formation of our present medical science.

On the threshold of these developments stands Andreas Vesalius, and today, four hundred years after the publication of his great book, we remember him in gratitude and pay tribute to his memory.

Vesalius belongs to many countries. His family came from Wesel in Lower Germany and moved later to Nymwegen in the Netherlands. He was born in Brussels, then the capital of the Netherlands, today the capital of Belgium. He studied medicine in France, was a professor in Italy, printed his book in Switzerland, was physician to the imperial court in Spain and died on a Greek island. Every country has a claim to him and he thus symbolizes the unity of Western civilization.

Vesalius was born in the night of New Year's Eve 1514 to 1515. In 1914 the world was preparing to celebrate the four hundredth anniversary of his birth, but when the day came the lights had gone out and the world was plunged in war. Brussels, his birthplace, was invaded by foreign troops. Louvain, his alma mater, was sacked. It is a grim irony that today when we are celebrating the four hundredth anniversary of the publication of his great book, the world is at war again, destroying with improved weapons, with increased ferocity its common heritage.

Shall we sit down and despair? No, emphatically no. Just because we are living at such a trying moment of history and because we suffer from the destruction of timeless values, we must stand up and react against this savagery. Now if ever we must remember our past, the obligations it puts upon us. What are we fighting for, after all? Not for sources of raw materials, not for markets. We are fighting against a philosophy that is the negation of culture; fighting for freedom, for the liberation of the people of the world from the bonds of ignorance, poverty and disease; fighting to create the material conditions for culture, for the day when culture will not be the privilege of a small upper class but will be shared and carried and produced by the masses. In these dark days we must carry the torch.

There are people in this country who loudly assert that such celebrations should not be held in times of war, that they distract the attention from the major objective, the winning of victory, that all efforts should be directed toward the pursuit of the war. And yet these very people who are so eager to forget the past, to ignore the debt we owe to our ancestors, to abandon all cultural activities, often have enough time to play bridge and engage in other "non-essential" activities. They document by their attitude that culture to them is not a necessity like air and water, but merely a superficial ornament, good for normal times but one that may be discarded lightheartedly in a period of emergency, that is, when we need it most desperately.

I really fail to see why we should not come together on solemn occasions to commemorate an event of the past, to acknowledge a debt, to renew our faith in science, in mankind, in the ideals of our predecessors that are still our ideals today. What good will it do us to win a military victory if we are starved culturally, if our imagination and enthusiasm have been so stifled, that we no longer have the courage to stand up and build the world of tomorrow? The few hours that such a ceremony may cost will not affect the war effort, and we can make up for them easily by concentrating in our work. The few dollars that such a ceremony may cost will not affect the war economy. They would not be invested in war stamps—they are not enough for bonds anyway—because they are contributed by people who have no surplus incomes. On the contrary, their incomes are greatly reduced, but they would gladly contribute a few dollars for the inspiration they would derive from such an event.

Many universities have dropped their commencement exercises "for the duration." We older professors who have attended many such exercises in the past, probably agree that commencement was some kind of an ordeal—in peace-time. Today when we are engaged in a life and death struggle, when the future of mankind is at stake, commencement has assumed more significance than ever. Our graduating students are in uniform, ready to go to the battlefields, ready to bring the supreme sacrifice to their country. Their immediate future is not a question of material success or failure but a question of life or death. We, their teachers, after having lived and worked with them for a number of years, feel at such a crucial moment the urge to commune with them, to clasp their hand, and to tell them what we have so deeply at heart, to tell them that there has been created a bond between us that only death can break, that they may regard the university as their second home to which they may always return and which will welcome them at any time. Words that come from the heart, spoken at a moment when our young people are so receptive, will vibrate in them. They will recall them in the anguished moments preceding their first battle, in dark nights spent on patrol duty or watching the sea from the bridge. They will feel that they are not alone, that in addition to being members of a physical family they are members of a great institution that has its roots in the Middle Ages and leads into a bright future. Instead of dropping commencement exercises "for the duration," universities should have availed themselves of this unique opportunity, should have developed a new ritual, and from a stereotyped dull performance should have made commencement the most stirring and inspiring event in the student's life—now if ever.

It speaks for our country that the publication of a great medical book, in the small city of Basle, four hundred years ago, was deemed important enough to call for nation-wide celebrations in the midst of a world war.

The New York Academy of Medicine inaugurated the series of exercises when its Section of Historical and Cultural Medicine held a Vesalius meeting on January 13. The Cleveland Branch of the Army Medical Library arranged a remarkable Vesalius Exhibit at and in cooperation with the Cleveland Medical Library. The Regional Meeting of Medical Librarians held in Philadelphia on June 10 and 11 devoted a whole session to the commemoration of Vesalius. Festive Vesalius meetings were held by the Academy of Medicine of Rochester, in Rochester, N. Y., on June 16, by the California Academy of Sciences in San Francisco on October 6, by the Washington Academy of Sciences on November 18. Vesalius was commemorated by the William Welch Society of New York University College of Medicine, by the University of West Virginia School of Medicine and by a number of other universities including the Ecole Libre des Hautes Etudes, the French University in exile, where George Sarton was the speaker.

On October 30 the Historical Library of Yale University School of Medicine held a formal academic exercise with an outstanding symposium on Vesalius and an exhibit that displayed some of the riches of the Cushing Collection. On November 1st the Johns Hopkins Medical History Club began the 54th year of its activities with a Vesalius celebration for which occasion the Institute of the History of Medicine had prepared an exhibit illustrating the life and work of the great anatomist.

The *Bulletin of the Medical Library Association* devoted its entire July number to Vesalius. The *Yale Journal of Biology and Medicine* published the papers read at the Yale Symposium. The most valuable publication of the year, however, was Harvey Cushing's posthumous *Bio-Bibliography of Andreas Vesalius* which with Moritz Roth's biography and M. H. Spielmann's iconography will constitute the iron foundation for all research on Vesalius.

The *Bulletin of the History of Medicine,* desirous of contributing its share, devoted its December number to Vesalius. It contained the papers read before the Johns Hopkins Medical History Club, two papers presented at the Research Conference of the Institute of the History of Medicine on November 2 and a number of other papers pertaining to the subject.

Let us hope that the four-hundredth anniversary of the death of Vesalius will be celebrated in 1964 in a pacified, rejuvenated and joyful world.

6

The University's Dilemma

OUR UNIVERSITIES will soon be facing an extremely critical situation which, I hasten to say, is entirely independent from the war. It began to manifest itself long before the outbreak of hostilities, but after the war when the universities will endeavor to resume their normal activities, they will become aware of this new situation in a very acute way.

The point, to put it briefly, is this: in continental Europe since the beginning of the 19th century, in some countries even before, and in the United States during the last fifty years, the ambition of a young researcher was to be appointed to a full professorship and to become head of a department. Such a position gave him the best possible opportunities to develop his talents and to build up a school. It gave him an audience, prestige, security and even comforts. Whenever a chair was vacant, the university called the best man available and usually obtained him. First consideration was given to his abilities as a researcher because research, the advancement of science and learning, was considered the modern university's primary function. It was often assumed and usually correctly, that a good researcher is a man who thinks clearly, and that a man who thinks clearly can express himself clearly and therefore must be a good teacher. The European university developed a tradition of academic oratory that was passed on from master to student and produced many brilliant academic teachers.

In Germany a certain hierarchy of universities developed during the 19th century. A young researcher began his career wherever he happened to be, usually at the university where he received his specialized training. If he proved to be a solid researcher who made some important contributions, he could count on being called as full professor to one of the smaller universities. There he was independent and had an ideal opportunity to develop his personality and skills as an original researcher. Those who did not grow with the new job remained where they were, the others were called to larger uni-

Written in 1943.

versities and the best men ended up as professors and department heads in Berlin, Munich or Leipzig, universities which for many decades could boast of having on their faculties the cream of the nation. After the first World War, there was in Prussia a tendency to specialize the universities, by crowding the best mathematicians and physicists in Göttingen, or the best oriental scholars in Breslau. Smaller universities often had a large turnover of faculty members but they rejoiced at having had some of the nation's outstanding researchers for a number of years and were proud of having them called to the country's greatest universities.

In Austria, Switzerland, Holland, and the Scandinavian countries where the universities followed the German pattern more or less, conditions were similar. In highly centralized France, young research-ers of talent flocked to the capital but the Collège de France, that unique institution, did not hesitate to appoint scholars occasionally from the provinces.

In the United States small universities which had little to offer had hardly any choice and had to content themselves with local people. Large universities, however, with good research facilities such as libraries, laboratories and hospitals could afford here as in Europe to canvass the whole country and succeeded in attracting the best researchers that were available. The original faculty of the Johns Hopkins School of Medicine had not one local man as head of a department and consisted of brilliant young researchers called from New York, Philadelphia, Chicago, Harvard and Michigan.

All this represented a very sound development. Today, however, we are facing a new and very disturbing situation. Our universities have grown and have become huge conglomerates of buildings, with large top-heavy departments. The position of full professor and head of a department has become an administrative position that consumes much time and energy and is no longer tempting to real researchers. If, however, we have to fill our most important chairs with men who are primarily interested in administrative work and not in research, the university will suffer irreparable damage.

I think the Western university is going to meet one of its greatest crises in history and the purpose of this paper is to raise a cry of alarm and to urge educators who are aware of their responsibilities to devote careful attention to the problem. Unless we can exercise sufficient imagination to find a solution, and courage to open up new paths, the university will degenerate, will lose its significance and become a mere routine educational mill.

It is not the first time that the Western university found itself in a critical situation and a brief historical analysis may therefore help in clarifying our thought.

*

When the mediaeval university was flourishing in the first half of the 13th century, it owned no property, had no buildings, no salaried employees but was a free association of teachers and students. They came together at the professor's home, or rented a room somewhere, or met in annex rooms of churches. The very poverty of the university was its strength because it was thus made independent. If conditions became unfavorable, teachers and students moved out and settled in some other city. More than one university was founded as a result of such migrations.

The early university did not require equipment. Its purpose was to transmit a body of knowledge, to keep traditions pure, to interpret and evaluate them. All that was needed were a few books. The professor lectured, that is, read from books and commented upon the subject. The students wrote down what they heard, or disputations were held.

Students were poor and benefactors from the middle of the 13th century on donated colleges, buildings in which students could live. The universities became property holders, many became wealthy. They made rules and regulations, established traditions and rituals. They had been granted privileges that they jealously guarded.

When the great awakening of the Renaissance came, when a new social and economic order began to shake the foundations of the Middle Ages, appealing to the individual in man and stirring him into rebellion against the traditional authorities, the universities—most of them—instead of taking the lead, looked backward, became strongholds of conservatism and clung desperately to mediaeval forms.

Anatomy, the public dissection of a human body, had been accepted by the universities from the early 14th century on, as a demonstration that illustrated traditions. Anatomy continued to be accepted when it became more than a demonstration, namely a field of research and exploration. It continued to be accepted because it already had a tradition of two hundred years. Vesalius did his crucial work at the university of Padua and most anatomists of the 16th century were connected with universities. It was difficult to procure cadavers outside of recognized institutions.

But in the 16th century already scientific research was cultivated outside of the universities. The great humanist physician, Fracastoro, was not a professor but a country doctor who practised in the neighborhood of Verona. Copernicus made a living as administrator of an estate. Paracelsus once tried to be a professor but it is well known what a dismal failure his short academic period at Basle was. Conrad Gesner, the "new Aristotle" was municipal physician at Zurich, and of the fathers of botany only one, Leonhard Fuchs, was connected with universities where he had troubles enough; Brunfels was municipal physician at Berne and Bock was primarily a preacher. The mathematician, Cardanus, made a living as a lawyer and John Weyer, who so courageously opposed witch-hunting, was physician-in-ordinary at the court of the Dukes of Berg. Surgery was renovated not by professors of surgery, but by barber-surgeons such as Ambroise Paré.

Even the humanities flourished more at the courts than in the universities and as early as the 15th century Marsiglio Ficino's Platonic Academy was certainly more inspiring than the *Studium generale* of Florence.

The university which for several centuries had been the centre of learning, the focus of intellectual activities, was unable to adjust itself to changing conditions. At a time when a new science was born and new approaches were found to the humanities, the university remained oriented toward the past, a remnant of feudalism in a new world.

The Reformation destroyed the harmony of the mediaeval university but was unable to create a new type of school that would have been broad enough to include the new science. And when this new science took its great development in the 17th century, it created for itself new centres, outside of the universities, the academies. In 1603 the Accademia dei Lincei was founded in Rome. Galileo was its dominating personality. He and his associates dreamed of a new type of research organization, scientific non-monastic monasteries, a brotherhood of scientists, with chapters in every country and every city. They anticipated Bacon's House of Solomon. In Florence, the Accademia del Cimento, founded in 1651, became a great centre of research. The Royal Society was chartered in England in 1662, and similar organizations were created thereafter in one country after another. They cultivated not only the natural sciences but the humanities as well. The Dictionary of the French Language was and still is a major project of the French Academy.

All this does not mean that the universities were entirely devoid of researchers. Galileo was for many years a professor at the universities of Pisa and Padua. Newton was professor of physics at Cambridge from 1669 to 1701. Scientists, after all, had to make a living and teaching was one way of doing it. But it is characteristic that all of them did not remain professors. An academic position was not the fulfillment of a researcher's ambitions.

Taken as a whole, the European universities had reached a rather low standard in the 17th century. They were educational institutions which produced average ministers, teachers, lawyers and physicians. Molière's bitter satires ridiculed a type of doctor who had remained mediaeval in a modern world.

Traditionalism always was the curse of the universities. They became rigid by necessity whenever they looked to the past and adhered to a social order that no longer existed instead of being major contributing factors in the shaping of the future. There is no reason why we should not remember our origins, and academic gowns, though slightly ridiculous today, are harmless as long as they are not taken too seriously. The University of Zurich in Switzerland, founded in 1833 as a stronghold of liberalism, never adopted the custom of wearing gowns. The University of Leipzig abolished it deliberately in the 18th century, repudiating the spirit that seemed embodied in a mediaeval costume, and it is highly characteristic that Leipzig reintroduced the wearing of gowns at the time when Hitler came into power.

*

In the 18th century under the influence of the philosophy of enlightenment, universities again became active centres of research. Protestant universities, less burdened by the mediaeval tradition,

paved the way. With the rise of the middle class the need for new
schools was felt and some of them were organized as centres of
research from the very start. In this development new universities
such as Halle and Göttingen played a very important part. The latter
was organized by a chancellor of genius, Baron Münchhausen, who
succeeded in assembling an extraordinary faculty of promising young
scientists and scholars, that included such men as Albrecht Haller.
They founded the Göttingen Academy of Science not as a competing
but as a supplementing body that gave them a forum, a link with
researchers of other countries and important means of publication.
The example set by Göttingen made a deep impression and other
universities became aware of the necessity of reorganizing their over-
aged institutions.

Haller was a graduate of Leyden where he had been under the
spell of Boerhaave's magnetic personality. Boerhaave's method of
clinical instruction revolutionized medical education. Students of his
founded the Medical School of Edinburgh and reorganized university
education in Austria. When the remnants of feudalism were over-
thrown by the French Revolution and the middle class came into
power, the universities were stirred into action. Latin was abolished
as the language of instruction. Old academic rites that had lost their
meaning were abandoned, new curricula were devised and the university became the modern researcher's paradise. It gave him clinics,
laboratories, libraries, the tools of research. It gave him an audience
and helpers and gave him a modest but secure income.

In many countries, the process was slow. It was relatively easy
to open up new schools, and many new universities were founded
during the 19th century, but it was difficult to close old and obsolete
ones. Italy and Spain were littered with old *Studia generalia,* many
of which could not live and could not die. They remained ill-equipped
and the professors were so poorly paid that they had to make a living
through outside activities.

The pattern of the modern university, however, was set. Students
were instructed by men who were actively engaged in research and
it was in the universities that the sciences took their great development. The very progress of science led to an increasing specialization
of research and consequently also of instruction. Johannes Müller was
professor of anatomy, physiology and pathology at the University

of Berlin, and with simple equipment and few assistants, he was able to make basic contributions to every one of these fields. When he died in 1858, it was obvious that no one individual would be able to carry on, and three chairs and three departments had to be established to take the place of the former one. Reichert was appointed to the chair of anatomy, Du Bois-Reymond to that of physiology and Rudolf Virchow had already been made professor of pathological anatomy the year before. He had a very versatile personality and made great contributions not only to pathology but also to anthropology. He was able to inspire and supervise the researches of his associates, to teach students, to conduct the pathological work of a large hospital, the Charité, to be himself in charge of a clinical division and he was, moreover, for many years a member of the Prussian Diet. He could engage in these many activities because he was an indefatigable worker and had a large and increasingly specialized staff.

Hygiene had its first organization department in Munich with Pettenkofer in 1865. The field grew and called for special departments of vital statistics, bacteriology, immunology, epidemiology, sanitary engineering, industrial hygiene, mental hygiene, health administration, health education. Special schools of hygiene and public health were founded.

Increasing specialization took place in the social sciences also. Subjects that used to be covered by philosophy and history branched off, and today we have in our universities large departments of social anthropology, sociology, economics, political science, and special schools of journalism. The humanities, with the rise of archaeology and the inclusion of more and more cultural areas, underwent a similar development.

As a result of the increase of knowledge and the necessary specialization of research, our universities have become conglomerations of schools with a great number of large departments. They all have collections because they must accumulate the materials and tools not only for present but also for future research. They serve as centres of information not only for members of the university but for outside students, for the community and the state. The head of the department is responsible for the collecting and adequate preservation of research materials. He must balance his budget or must stretch it so that it will meet the needs of the department. He advises the members of his staff in their research, must raise the money for special projects, for the printing of publications, and he is frequently editor of journals and other serial publications. He teaches post-graduate, graduate and sometimes also under-graduate students, gives them examinations, advises them and helps them in finding jobs. He must attend meetings inside and outside the university and is heavily burdened with committee work.

The professor who is head of a department has thus become primarily an administrator, and we all know dozens of distinguished men whose research career ended the day they were appointed to some famous chair as a reward for outstanding researches.

Theoretically, the professor can delegate functions to members of his staff, and he may have young people with him who have administrative ability and like this kind of work. This, however, is usually not the case because young people are appointed to the staff not for their administrative skills but for the promise they show as researchers.

A chair and department are still tempting to many young scholars and scientists because they represent a very gratifying recognition of previous work and promise prestige, a higher salary at a time when the family is growing, and research facilities. Young people are inclined to underestimate the administrative burden that is in store for them, or they think that they will be able to handle matters better than their former chiefs did. Soon enough they find themselves involved in an inextricable mesh and many give up or stop in their development. How often does it not happen that a man after he has reached the highest step in the academic ladder never produces a new idea but merely continues along the trodden path? He no longer has any leisure, no time to look around and to think. His life has become an endless series of appointments, with secretaries waiting for dictation.

I have no doubt that in the future it will become increasingly difficult to fill chairs with first-rate researchers. They will seek outlets in other institutions. When this day comes, the university will find itself in an extremely critical position.

*

The present crisis is basically different from that which befell the university in the 16th and 17th centuries. At that time the university was unable to accept the new science and remained mediaeval in a modern world. Today the new science and learning are not only accepted by the universities but have developed in and largely because of them. The specialization of research was a process that took place right in the university. But this very development of specialized research has created a new situation, and if the university takes a conservative attitude, clinging to the traditions it established from the 18th century on, if it fails to adjust itself to the new conditions, the result will be the same as it was in the previous crisis: research will be divorced from the university.

Long ago institutions were created that permitted a scholar to pursue his researches without being burdened by administrative duties. The Collège de France is the outstanding example. The Rockefeller Institute for Medical Research, the Brookings Institute, the Institute of Advanced Study in this country, the Kaiser Wilhelm Institute in Germany, the Zoological Station at Naples, the various Archaeological Institutes in Greece and Italy, to mention only a few, were founded as centres of research outside the universities. Industry created great and lavishly equipped laboratories. Government departments organized research institutions in many countries.

Great contributions have come from all these centres. They have more than justified their existence and nobody would wish to be without them. They play a very important part in the life of a nation—as long as they do not replace research in universities but supplement it.

If the universities are not able to make adjustments, the future trend is all too obvious: more independent research institutes will be founded; they will attract and absorb the creative forces and will play the part that the academies played in the 17th century. The universities, on the other side, will become educational mills imparting secondhand knowledge.

This, however, would be a most detrimental course. Why? Because university education becomes sterile the moment it is divorced from research. History has demonstrated this over and over again. What makes higher education is just the fact that young people are granted the privilege to spend a number of years at the source of learning in close touch with men whose life-work is devoted to the advancement of knowledge.

The researcher, on the other hand, who is not in touch with stu-

The University's Dilemma

dents loses a great deal.[1] The professor becomes older every year but his students remain eternally young, and this contact with a constantly rejuvenating mankind is a great stimulus to him. It makes him look beyond the boundary of his generation, and he who in his research is working for the future, with and through his students, can help in shaping tomorrow's world. And when he follows them up in their professional life and sees the seed germinating, he feels a satisfaction equal to that of having procreated children.

The researcher who presents the results of his work before a scientific society addresses specialists who are familiar with the problems involved. They will understand him even if his presentation is not too clear. The researcher who, as an academic teacher, addresses students is forced to think his problems to the end and to formulate and present them simply and clearly. The teaching of students, therefore, is extremely valuable to the researcher, provided there is not too much of it and it does not degenerate into routine.

And so the university's dilemma appears clearly before our eyes: the specialization of research, the growth of individual disciplines and consequently of university departments has created a new situation. Either we let things go with the result that research will gradually desert the university, or we find a solution that will make an academic appointment as attractive to the researcher as it was in the past.

What then is the solution?

*

I am sorry to say that I have no ready-made answer to offer. The purpose of this article is not to outline a solution of the problem but rather to raise and formulate it.

The problem was felt long ago and some steps have already been taken in various places toward its solution. The establishment of the full-time system in clinical departments was undoubtedly a step in the right direction in that it liberated clinical professors from the economic bonds of private practice. But even without private practice, the head of a clinical department is heavily burdened with a load of

[1] I have purposefully not mentioned the great research institutions of the Soviet Union such as the Academy of Science of the U. S. S. R. or the All-Union Institute of Experimental Medicine because there the situation is totally different. The Soviet research institutions are deeply rooted in the life of the nation and members of such institutes are always in close touch with students, factory workers and farmers.

administrative work, and today the number of clinicians who remain creative and fertile researchers once they are in charge of a department is not very large. The best they can do as a rule is to stimulate research and have it carried out by members of their staff whereby it is difficult to tell how much credit is due to the chief and how much to his assistants.

Some time ago, the Rockefeller Foundation established a number of clinical research fellowships named in honor of Dr. William H. Welch. Unlike other fellowships, they are given for a period of three years that may be extended to six years, and carry a generous stipend which permits the fellow to live on a decent standard. The very sound idea was to give talented young people an opportunity to engage for a relatively long period of time in clinical research and to prepare themselves for an academic career without financial worries. The only trouble is that if a Welch Fellow fulfills the expectations set on him, he will be rewarded with an administrative job which will be the heavier the more brilliant his researches have been. I think it would be worthwhile to consider the extension of such a fellowship to ten or even twenty years if a man shows particular aptitude for research.

The University of Minnesota established "Distinguished Service" chairs and Yale has special Sterling professorships for meritorious scholars. They carry the salary of a full professor without imposing any obligations. As a rule, however, they are given to retiring professors, and a man should not have to wait so long before he is given the opportunity to devote himself entirely to research.

Academic administrative work is very important and I am far from underestimating its value. Without it, departments would simply disintegrate and become worthless as means of research. But it is a waste to impose it upon the main researcher of the department, just as it is a waste to crush him with a heavy teaching schedule.

If the university is to remain an active centre of research imparting first-hand knowledge to students; if a university appointment is to remain attractive to researchers, we must think along new lines and must devise a different system. It must be one that will give the researcher time and leisure to engage in his studies, not only late at night when he is close to exhaustion. It must permit him to give few but significant courses on subjects that happen to be close to his heart.

It must give him time to meet with his colleagues and students, leisurely, not with an eye on the clock.

Specialization was unavoidable and was primarily responsible for the great advances in science and learning. It would be futile romanticism to dream of going back to the good old days when the professor worked at home in his private library or in the private laboratory he had in the basement of his house.

The trend undoubtedly will be toward more specialization, and we may have to think of a department not in terms of a hierarchy but of a cooperative, highly specialized group in which the main researchers will have the least administrative burden.

I do not know what the best solution is but I know that we must find one, and that we must find it soon.

7

The University at the Crossroads

THE FUTURE of our universities cannot but fill us with deepest concern. The damage that the war has already inflicted on them is immeasurable and is growing with every year in geometric progression. Some universities have practically collapsed. Oh, their campuses are teeming with life or at least were until yesterday: thousands of students in uniform rose in the morning at the call of the bugle, marched to classes, learned anything under the sun in a few months, from meteorology to Chinese, passed examinations and joined the ranks.

It obviously was the duty of the universities to make their facilities available to the armed forces. In doing so they did not fare badly because they were compensated generously and because dormitories and classrooms were empty anyway. Now in 1943 that the Army Specialized Training Program is being discontinued, many colleges are lamenting and may have to close their doors altogether.

These activities should not deceive us, and we should keep in mind that the instruction given to A. S. T. P. students in our buildings has nothing in common with university education and that this teeming life actually unfolds itself on the ruins of the university.

In many schools great scholars were urged to drop their researches for the duration of the war—which may well be for their lifetime—and to devote all their energy to giving elementary courses to A. S. T. P. or V-12 students, courses that young 4-F instructors could have given just as well, if not better. In fields where instructors were unavailable this might have been justified, but in many cases it happened for purely mercenary reasons. Universities were compensated for these courses, and while they would have had to pay specially appointed instructors they had the services of their professors free and thus made a profit. The immeasurable and possibly irreparable loss is that many scholars' research careers have been wrecked perhaps forever.

Written in 1944.

The University at the Crossroads

Every war is conducted under a terrific wastage of manpower. In the field of research where reserves are so infinitely small, waste is fatal.

The professors answered the appeal to their patriotism without hesitation. They would have peeled potatoes if they had been asked to do so and if they had felt that it would help the war. Today already voices are being heard accusing them of having betrayed their mission by dropping their researches; of having rendered a disservice to their country by abandoning the work of a lifetime and agreeing to perform tasks for which they were unprepared and which dozens of other people could have performed just as well. They are told that they should have known better, that they should have taken the odium upon themselves, realizing that in the long run their work would have been of greater benefit to the country. No one thanks them for their sacrifices, but they can be sure that after the war they will hear a great deal about the *trahison des clercs*.

The conflict in which the professors found themselves was a serious one. All of them, without exception, wanted to contribute their share to the pursuit of the war, but all those who were not drafted had to decide for themselves in which way they could serve the country best. Those who were real researchers, who had devoted their entire life to the advancement of science and learning, were of course convinced of the significance of their work and knew that the greatest contribution they could possibly make was to stay where they were, to redouble their efforts and to keep the universities alive as the great cultural centers that the nation needs today and will need tomorrow more than ever.

Common decency forbade them to proclaim their own worth. Some, and among them some of the best, had doubts as to their capacities and as to the actual value of their work. This was the moment when the leadership was needed that failed to come forth. This was the moment when the universities needed presidents who were more than investment bankers, presidents who would gather their men, confirm them in their faith, lead and inspire them to ever greater achievements; presidents who would forbid scholars to accept clerical jobs in Washington and prevent professors of American history from serving in the Volunteer Coast Guard at a moment when the country is crying for intensified research and instruction in the field; presidents who would prevent philosophers from learning Japanese or Siamese while the country is in dire need of philosophic orientation.

I know of a few, a very few, university presidents who acted that way. The majority stampeded to Washington the day after Pearl Harbor, offering their services to the government. They dropped their universities like a dead weight with an alacrity that was, to say the least, disconcerting. Many of them, I am sure, were thinking in terms of a short war, because the last war had been short. They overlooked the fact that World War II had begun on September 18, 1931, when Japanese troops had occupied Mukden. They overlooked the fact that it was by mere accident that we entered so late and that we may well be engaged in the war, directly or indirectly, for a dozen more years. They all, of course, were motivated by the noblest patriotism; but when a ship is hit by the greatest storm it has ever experienced, the captain's place is on the bridge and not on shore. There are some presidents whose expert advice is absolutely essential to the government. Their obvious duty is to serve the government and to leave the drowning ship in the command of the first mate, without trying to control it from a distant position on shore.

Once university presidents had dropped their schools, it was only logical for them to urge their professors to drop their researches also and to demonstrate their patriotism by—peeling potatoes. This is one reason why the university finds itself in such a critical position today. There are many others.

*

The present war requires that a large number of soldiers possess a great variety of specialized skills which must be acquired in a minimum of time. Ingenious teaching methods have been devised and the results have been surprisingly good. Members of university faculties have played an important part in developing these programs and now many of them, blinded by the results obtained, are inclined to believe that these same methods could be applied to university education.

A discussion that I had some time ago with a colleague who had once been a scholar and had now been teaching in the army for two years, was shockingly revealing. He gave me a glowing account of his work and pictured how after the war these new teaching methods would revolutionize the university. With due respect for his uniform

[68]

I tried to point out that teaching in the army and teaching in the university were serving totally different purposes, that the army very appropriately was not talking of *education* but of *indoctrination*. The army wants soldiers to acquire in a minimum of time a generally accepted, dogmatic and standardized body of knowledge and skills that must be applied immediately to a useful purpose. If experience should show that the dogmas do not hold any longer, the soldiers would be given another indoctrination course with new dogmas.

This is about the opposite of what university teaching endeavors to be. We try to impress upon the students that there is no such thing as a generally accepted body of knowledge, that science and learning are evolving constantly, under our very eyes. We urge them not to accept authorities but to find out for themselves what things are like. We teach them methods of attaining knowledge and leave it to them to find the truth. We want them to develop a critical attitude toward the world and to develop their own philosophy of life.

In teaching languages our purpose is not to enable the student to express himself fluently in foreign baby-talk but to give him the key to a critical appreciation of foreign literatures.

There can be no doubt that after the war, efforts will be made to force methods upon the university that are foreign to its very essence, by individuals who believe that phonograph records and movies can replace thinking. We must be prepared to resist these attacks vigorously. That does not mean that the university has no use for technical devices, far from it. Records, movies, photostats and microfilms are valuable tools for research and teaching as long as they are means to an end and not the end itself. When the World War reached Europe the most fantastic microfilm projects came up in this country. We were told quite seriously that over a million books should be microfilmed. I was asked by a learned agency what mediaeval manuscripts I urgently needed for my researches. I have been working on early mediaeval medical manuscripts for over twenty years and there are still a good many that I would like to see some day, but my reply was that I could do very well without any manuscript and that I could keep myself and my students busy for at least fifty years investigating and interpreting those mediaeval medical texts that have been printed from the 15th century on and can be found in any American library. We are always preparing for research by making dictionaries, catalogues, bibliographies, concordances, indices, atlases, at a terrific expense of money. Why not take advantage of the war and do the research for a change, using the tools?

We were unprepared for the war and therefore had to build up an enormous army overnight. Speed was essential and every existing program was accelerated. We are training physicians in three calendar years, and while we used to require a completed college course we are now satisfied with a rudimentary preparation of less than two years. We have waived language requirements and feel gratified when the students are able to handle their mother tongue. This accelerated program was put into effect with hardly any discussion. Once a few schools had adopted it the others had to follow suit since they were all competing for students. It was practically forced upon us and opposition would have been considered unpatriotic. It may be justified as an emergency measure, but already we hear educators, medical and others, talk of speeding up programs after the war before we know what the effect of the present acceleration has been.

There is no doubt that time is wasted, but not in the graduate school. The waste is to be found before and afterwards, in the undergraduate school and during the years that it takes before a man is fully employed. There we could save time, but not in the graduate school. Graduate education is a slow process of assimilation and maturation. It is not the number of courses and hours that counts but the work that the student puts in, and he needs time, to read, to think and to gain experience.

After the war we shall have hundreds of thousands of half-trained and actually uneducated young people who will all know a few tricks in physics, chemistry, engineering or other fields. They will constitute a serious problem and we must be prepared to meet it. Having been on a campus for some time and having gained practical experience in the war, they will be inclined to consider themselves experts, not realizing how one-sided and superficial their training has been. Actually we shall have a multitude of technicians but very few educated people.

The whole question of personnel for research and teaching in universities will be an extremely critical one. We have hardly any graduate students today—outside of medical, dental and engineering schools—which means that we shall have no instructors tomorrow and no young professors ten years from now. Many young people in the armed forces who intended to embark on a research career will find after the war that they have become too old to start at the bottom again. They are probably married, may have a couple of children by the time the war is over, and the prospect of living with a family for ten or more years on the meagre stipend of a fellowship or instructorship will not be very encouraging.

It is quite safe to predict that the great majority of the more mature faculty members who are in the armed forces or engaged in some other kind of war work, are lost for research. They will come back, most of them, will resume their teaching in a routine way using their pre-war lecture notes, will write a paper here and there but they will soon find that they have lost touch with scholarship. A man who has abandoned his laboratory or study for a number of years rarely finds the way back. There will be exceptions to the rule and there are professors, particularly in science, whose war work is in the same field as their normal civilian work, but their number is not large and the casualties will be heavy.

And as to the professors who are too old for the armed forces and are carrying on in the universities today, in research and teaching, working day and night under terrific strain, doing their own and their colleagues' work, they will be used up after the war and we should not expect much from them. Once the tension is over, many will break down.

A young generation, of course, will grow up, will enter the universities, will engage in research with the same enthusiasm that animated their predecessors, but in the meantime we must count with a serious gap.

*

The factors discussed so far are the immediate result of the war, but there are unfortunately other disintegrating forces at work that have been threatening the university long before the war broke out.

The universities are, or should be, the nation's most important centres of research. Academic research in a free country is characterized by the fact that it is seeking the truth for the truth's sake, irrespective of whether the results may have any practical consequences or not. It has nothing to sell, no ax to grind, no thesis to prove. Researchers have different philosophies and their views may clash at times, but it is believed that the very clash of ideas, the frank unrestrained academic discussion is a way to bring us closer to the truth.

Academic instruction is first-hand instruction based on the findings of academic research and conveyed by teachers who are researchers themselves.

It is very disturbing to find that the universities are anxiously avoiding touching upon any subject that seems in the least controversial. I shall give only two examples but they will reveal how serious the situation is.

For twenty-five years the subject of the Soviet Union was practically non-existent in our universities. The Russian language that provides the key to an understanding of Soviet civilization was hardly taught. Only few large universities had adequate Slavic departments. In some others, elementary courses were given by instructors who were not philologists and whose only qualification was that their mother tongue had once been Russian. In some schools courses in Russian literature were given, often by refugees who could not see beyond Alexander Blok if they ever went that far. In many universities the department of political science offered occasionally a course announced under some such title as "European dictatorships: fascism, nazism, communism." It is needless to say that these courses were given as a rule on the basis of second-hand information by men who had never undertaken any serious researches in the field.

There was a great country covering one-sixth of the inhabited earth, in which the most significant event of the first World War had taken place; a country that was making a tremendous effort to apply principles of science to the basic processes of social life, to production, distribution, consumption; a country that was building a new society on the foundation of a new economy, was carrying education to the most remote mountain villages of Central Asia, was entering upon new paths in agriculture, in public health and many other fields.

It sounds almost incredible that the study of events of such magnitude that touched every field of human endeavor should have been banned from our universities. And yet it was true, and professors who on their own account engaged in research on some aspect of Soviet civilization were frequently insulted and persecuted for having dared to break a taboo. The Soviet Union was considered a controversial subject and the university was to be kept pure of such subjects. It was, moreover, a challenge, and students were not to be challenged.

When the U. S. S. R. was invaded by German armies and did not collapse within a few weeks as military "experts" had prognosticated, public opinion in this country was suddenly stirred and people realized that they had been kept uninformed or had been grossly misinformed about that country. And once the Soviet people had become our most powerful ally, it was obvious that in the future we would have much closer dealings with them and that there would be a great demand for Americans who not only could read and speak Russian but would be familiar with Soviet institutions. And yet not a single university in this country was prepared to give academic instruction on the subject.

The Rockefeller Foundation, which in this as in so many other fields proved to be more progressive and farsighted than most of our institutions of learning, invited universities to give courses on the Soviet Union and offered to provide part of the costs. One university answered the call, and in the summer of 1943, Cornell University took the pioneering step by announcing a sixteen-week course "Intensive Study of Contemporary Russian Civilization," directed by Professor Ernest J. Simmons. It was an educational experiment and not an easy one. A faculty had to be assembled from all sections of the country; it was to consist of men who were thoroughly familiar with the U. S. S. R. and had devoted many years of research to some aspect of Soviet civilization so that instruction would be of high academic standard.

The course was a tremendous success. Faculty and students, aware of their responsibility and of the unusual educational opportunity presented, worked very hard and with great enthusiasm. The Soviet Union was studied in all its aspects but only after a solid historical foundation had been laid. The course was to be repeated in 1944, at Cornell and in another great university of the country. But in the meantime the unavoidable had happened: a university had dared to touch upon a controversial subject, one moreover that might be interpreted as a challenge to our most sacred economic dogmas. A professional red-baiter launched a smear campaign. Cornell was pictured as a hotbed of subversive activities. The charges were, of course, ridiculous but the fact could not be denied that a great university had dared to offer academic instruction to young people on a contemporary subject of vital importance and that this was a subject about which there was not a general consensus of opinion. Trustees and alumni became alarmed. Universities are like beautiful women; they wish to be admired but not talked about. For a while it looked as if the course could not be repeated. But it was repeated in 1944, and I think the whole country owes a profound debt of gratitude to Cornell University and its president, Edmund E. Day, for having demonstrated forcefully, in spite of all the pressure brought upon them, that the American university, at least one of them, is aware of its responsibility, that it wishes to remain an active center of dispassionate research and instruction even in controversial fields, and that it is not at the mercy of newspaper slander.[1]

Another example: one of the most acute medical and social problems today is that of the distribution of medical care and of the organization of medical services. Everyone knows by now that great changes have occurred during the last fifty years in medicine as well as in society. As a result of the great development of science, medicine has become highly technical, highly specialized and very effective, but at the same time the cost of medical care has increased more rapidly than the purchasing power of the population. Society, on the other hand, as a result of industrialization, has become highly differentiated, highly specialized also, a society of wage earners who depend for a living on the labor market and have no security of income. It seems pretty obvious that a new medical science called upon to serve a new type of society requires new forms of medical service. Social adjustments must be made to meet the conditions created by the new technology.

The question of security in matters of health is but one aspect of the great problem of social security which has become the major domestic war aim in all Western countries. It is not a radical but a conservative issue, because it accepts the existing order and conserves it by providing a corrective mechanism without which it would collapse sooner or later. The alternative to social security legislation is social unrest and even revolution.

The provision of complete and first-rate medical services to the

---

[1] We hear that the State of New York will establish at Cornell University a "School of Labor and Industrial Relations," another controversial subject that Cornell is not afraid to approach.

entire population in town and country obviously presents a difficult problem, one that requires a great deal of research before final legislative action can be taken. It is complicated research that calls for the combined efforts of physicians, public health experts, sociologists and economists. Indeed, the most ingenious economic plan is worthless if it is used to finance a poor type of medical service, and the best devised medical plan must by necessity collapse if it is not financed properly.

The universities, equipped as they are with all facilities for research, with outstanding medical and public health men, economists, sociologists, political scientists on their faculties would have been the logical centers to engage in the research that the country so urgently needed. And yet, with very few exceptions, they refused to touch the problem. Why? Because it was a controversial subject, one that seemed to affect vested interests, one about which conservative and liberal opinion disagreed. The research that had to be done was therefore left to private groups and to government agencies.

The universities, having failed to engage in research in the sociology and economics of medicine, were obviously unprepared to provide instruction in the field and this at a moment when students were crying for it. The fact that health insurance and similar issues are discussed in medical circles in such an amateurish and emotional way is owing to lack of education. Unprepared by the university, the doctor finds himself at the mercy of propaganda agencies. We should expect that the university would learn from these shortcomings and would endeavor to train a young medical generation prepared to meet or at least to understand the social problems of medicine. But where there is no research there cannot be academic instruction. Some schools announced a course that was given by an instructor who happened to be interested in the subject and willing to read a few books. But it was second-hand instruction of little value. In other schools the students organized their own study groups and since the faculty was unable to help them, they worked hard trying to find the facts without guidance through their own efforts.

If the university persists in ignoring some of the most vitally important subjects on account of their controversial nature, the unavoidable result will be that independent research institutions will be founded outside of the university. It is obvious that research and instruction in such fields as the Soviet Union or the sociology and economics of medicine cannot be left to propaganda agencies and pressure groups. The country needs information based on dispassionate scholarly research and workers trained in these subjects in the academic way. If the university fails the nation, enlightened foundations will help, since the need is an urgent one, to create independent Institutes of Slavic Studies and Institutes of Medical Economics. The nation will be served, but the university will find itself greatly impoverished.

If, however, research should become increasingly divorced from the university, it would mean the end of the graduate school, and the university would become a routine educational mill imparting a traditional, non-controversial, generally accepted and orthodox body of knowledge to undergraduate students, and training technicians for various professions. It would soon degenerate to the level of a dignified secondary and technical school.

*

The university finds itself at the crossroads indeed and is facing one of its greatest crises. The disintegrating forces that are assailing it from all sides are overwhelming, but it is not too late. The university can be saved if we are determined to save it and can bring up enough courage and imagination. Many universities, aware of the danger, have appointed committees for the study of their post-war problems. They have a tremendous responsibility and the future may well be determined by their actions. They must realize that conditions have changed radically in the last fifty years and that the mere patching up of curricula is not a solution. They must be prepared to recommend basic, revolutionary changes in the very structure of the university and must not be afraid of totally new departures.

This is not the place to outline a program but I would like to stress a few general principles which, in my opinion, must be observed under any circumstances.

First of all: the universities and particularly the graduate schools must remain the nation's most active centers of independent scholarly research, and must be ready to approach any important subject even if it should happen to be controversial at a given moment. Their work may be supplemented by that of independent research institutions but should not be replaced by it because such a development would be fatal to the university. Researchers should be given positions that will permit them to engage in research and will not burden them with a heavy load of administrative duties which consume most of their time and energy. The university needs many able administrators, but a system must be found that will permit a division of labor and will not place the main administrative burden upon the main researchers. It is an inexcusable waste to have a man spend twenty and more years acquiring knowledge and experience in a field of learning and then compel him to spend his time devising wage-scales of charwomen and janitors, pondering about the upkeep of grounds, or spending hours discussing with committees whether a set of windows should have Venetian blinds or not.

Graduate schools, to be sure, must train students for professions, must prepare them to play their part in society as teachers, physicians, scientists, lawyers, ministers, or engineers. But graduate education must be infinitely more than the imparting of technical knowledge. It must be education. One of the main reasons for the collapse of civilization and reversal into primitive savagery that we are experiencing today lies in the fact that in most countries the leaders were highly trained specialists who knew nothing outside of their specialty and were totally unable to correlate it with any other aspect of life. How often does it not happen that a great surgeon, a great lawyer, the president of a bank, the president of a large industrial corporation, a senator, or a cabinet minister, great specialists as they are, have no more general education than their janitor or night watchman? The university gave them nothing but specialized training, and thereafter life became so absorbing that there was no time for reading and thinking and meditating outside of their specialty. How can we expect such men to have sound political judgment and to be leaders in critical times?

And this is where the undergraduate school comes in. Its function is to lay a solid educational foundation. There are, of course, various methods of doing this. Personally I believe that tomorrow more than ever, we shall have to emphasize the study of the classics. There are no short-cuts in education. The mind must be trained before it can comprehend. The students, of course, should understand the society in which they live and are called upon to play an intelligent part. But how can they understand it unless they have first gone through the schools of Plato and Aristotle, of Descartes and Rousseau, of Adam

Smith and Karl Marx? They should understand the physical world in which they find themselves, but they must first train their minds on Euclid, Copernicus, Galileo, Leibnitz, Lavoisier, Darwin and others. A study of English literature justly begins not with D. H. Lawrence or T. S. Eliot but with Chaucer. A study of contemporary life without historical and philosophic foundations remains by necessity superficial and meaningless.

I would not be astonished if a good many returning soldiers, more than we commonly expect, would come back from a mechanized war in which they helped to destroy our common heritage, thirsting for the classics, for the eternal values that no bomb was able to destroy. In every war the sufferings and the proximity of death have changed the sense of values of many of the young people who experienced them. When they shall come to us we must not disappoint them.

The graduate school builds on the foundation laid by the undergraduate college. It must continue the educational work. It is obliged to impart specialized knowledge and skills but must do this in the academic way, that is in relation to the whole, as if it were studied for its own sake, without regard for immediate practical application. A medical, engineering, or law school that has no room for historical and philosophic studies can produce technicians at best but never educated citizens and educated specialists. The classics form the common ground on which specialists meet, and how could they cooperate unless they have a common ground on which to stand?

The university is at the crossroads, and we cannot view its future without deep apprehension. The need for it is undeniable, today more than ever, and it still has unbounded possibilities of development. But the disintegrating forces are strong and are particularly threatening to the graduate school. The tendency to emphasize quantity rather than quality is unfortunately still prevalent, and many people still believe that a university is the better the bigger it is, while the reverse is usually true. Much will depend on the plans that are being formulated now for the post-war period, and it is to be hoped that the planners are aware of the tremendous responsibility that has been placed upon them, and that they will look at the problems not from the narrow point of view of the individual campus but from the point of view of the nation at large, realizing also that the future of science and learning may well depend on whatever actions they take.

In the meantime, during these dark years of war, we must carry the torch and must maintain academic standards at any cost. Professors are few, and students are few, but among these few students, men and women, may be the leaders of tomorrow and they must not be deprived of educational opportunities. We must also remember that warfare is merely an instrument of politics and that politics is the result of philosophy.

8

The Study of Medicine in Wartime

IN MY DOUBLE capacity as William H. Welch Professor of the History of Medicine and Acting Librarian of the William H. Welch Medical Library, I take great pleasure in welcoming you to this building that houses two departments named in honor of a great man.

There has rarely been a wiser man than Dr. Welch. He joined the faculty of this University as early as 1884, five years before the Hospital was founded, nine years before the School of Medicine opened its doors. He was our first dean, a pathologist and bacteriologist of renown who created a great school of American pathology; a leader in the public health field, the first Director of our School of Hygiene and Public Health; a friend and adviser to generations of doctors. Whoever came in touch with him, young students and old physicians, were soon conquered by his gentle and kindly manner, remained forever attached to him and felt lasting inspiration.

Late in life Dr. Welch became the first professor of the history of medicine in our School and founded the Institute of the History of Medicine, the first department of its kind in the United States. Thus his creative mind was active from the beginning to the end of his career. He remained a builder, and at a time when other men think of retiring from the active scene, he was still looking into the future, opening up new fields, endeavoring to keep our School the pioneering institution it had been for so many years.

This building with its 150,000 volumes and 600 journals, in which the results of research converge once they have been formulated in writing, in which the experiences of centuries are accumulated, interpreted, and utilized in preparing for the future, is indeed a most fitting monument to the memory of Dr. Welch.

In entering our school you become links in a great tradition. Wherever you go you will encounter the names of Osler, Halsted,

Address to the entering class of the Johns Hopkins University School of Medicine, delivered on November 30, 1943.

Kelly, Welch, Mall, Howell, Abel, the men who just fifty years ago constituted the first faculty of our School. They were all young men, all under forty years of age, and with tremendous enthusiasm they set out to establish a new pattern of medical education in this country. It is hard for you to realize today how revolutionary this step was. At Hopkins in 1893 medical education had become graduate education. Students were no longer treated as children who had to be fed with a spoon, but as responsible adults. Women were admitted on equal terms with men. Instruction was given by teachers who were all actively engaged in research, and it was given not through lectures alone but primarily in the laboratory, at the bedside of patients and in seminar discussions. A new type of a scientifically trained physician was prepared, and the disciples of our first professors were soon holding distinguished positions all over the country.

A great tradition may be a most powerful stimulus, but it can also be a great handicap. Everything depends upon how you interpret it. John Billings, in reviewing a hundred years of American medicine in 1876, said that it was better to have a future than a past. I think it is still better to have both, a future and a past, provided you understand the past and are aware of the obligations it puts upon you.

A few years from now—all too soon—you will be Hopkins doctors, and you know that the Hopkins doctor has a good reputation in the world. If the fact that you are links in this great tradition should make you oriented toward the past, conservative, self-satisfied; if you should come to think that you are great doctors merely because you attended this school, because you can quote Osler, Welch and the others and tell stories about them: then indeed the tradition would have turned against you, would have become a heavy burden, and it would have been better for you to attend a young school that has a future but no past.

Things are different if you interpret the tradition correctly, if you are aware of the great obligation it puts upon you, the obligation to live up to it at any time. It is not by looking backward, by quoting and copying our great masters that you uphold the reputation of our school, but by looking bravely into the future and by attacking the new problems of medicine courageously with imagination and, I may say, in the same revolutionary spirit that animated our predecessors in medical matters. Facing a problem, do not ask: "What did Osler or Welch do?"—they did the right thing at their time. Ask rather: "How would they act today if they were with us, men of our generation, young and enthusiastic as they were in 1893?" Approached in such a way, a tradition becomes a rich source of inspiration, a driving force for constructive action.

A great deal has changed in the last fifty years. Medicine has progressed very rapidly, has become highly technical, highly specialized, and medical services have become very costly. We had a second industrial revolution that has changed the very structure of our American society. We have been involved in two world wars and can no longer confine ourselves within the borders of our country. At the same time the scope of medicine has broadened considerably and the physician is called upon for advice by the educator, the lawyer, the statesman. There is hardly any field of public life in which the doctor has not a voice. Today more than ever, it is a joy to be a physician.

This great development, however, raises a great many questions. The pattern of medical education that we set fifty years ago and that was subsequently adopted by most medical schools of the country, is it still valid today? Are we training the doctor that American society will need to-morrow, or are we still training the physician of yesterday? Was it enough to patch up the curriculum by adding a course here and there, or have we reached the point at which a new, a revolutionary departure is needed in medical education, as it was fifty years ago?

We must never rest, never be satisfied with what we are doing, never do a thing merely because we did it in the past. There is no greater impediment to progress than inertia and complacency. We are not afraid of experimenting in scientific matters and we are not afraid of negative results. We must summon the courage to experiment in the educational and social fields of medicine also. If we do not, the obvious will happen: some other school, in some other section of the country, will do exactly what we did fifty years ago, namely set a new pattern of medical education.

I wish to add that this is not a question of money. I know, of course, that other schools have greater financial resources than we have. But the very history of our school teaches us that where there is an imaginative, constructive program the money comes in. The idea, the vision, must by necessity come first.

*

You have come to us from a great variety of colleges, and I do not know how well prepared you are for graduate work. You have, of course, complied with all our present entrance requirements, but this is obviously not enough. A college education must give you more than mere technical knowledge. In the past we required a completed college course and a bachelor's degree. Some of you have it, others had three years and others only two years of college. But the qualities I have in mind may well be acquired in two years or may not be acquired in ten years. Let me explain what I mean by reading you a letter that I recently wrote. The dean of a Western college had written to a number of graduate school teachers asking them what they considered the best preparation for graduate study in their particular field. This was my answer:

"To put it briefly—what I expect of a college graduate is the following:

1. *Intellectual curiosity,* the thirst for knowledge. Do not take the world for granted but try to find out about it.

2. *Critical judgment.* Do not accept your teachers' words or the textbooks as authorities. Remember that they merely represent individual views. Do not be afraid of contradicting "authorities" if you think you have valid arguments. You must find the truth for yourself, and remember that this is a lifelong job.

3. *Imagination.* Experts will tell you what cannot be done. They may be right, but do not believe them. If you have ideas, stick to them. Progress begins with dreams and is achieved when they become reality. It is difficult to develop imagination in students but very easy to kill it.

4. *A correct sense of values.* Try to find out what is really important in life and what is not. And develop a positive attitude toward mental and physical health.

5. *Social consciousness.* Keep always in mind that you are a member of a society that grants you great privileges but toward which you have just as great obligations. Be ready to serve your fellowmen at any time with all your faculties, and remember that the welfare of the group is more important than your individual welfare.

6. *Correct use of the mother tongue.* Think clearly so that you may

express yourself clearly. Enrich your vocabulary and your practical knowledge of grammar daily by reading the great past and contemporary writers critically.

7. *Knowledge of working methods.* Learn to attain knowledge through observation, experiments, correct reasoning, the use of books and other tools. Do not work haphazardly but planfully. Set yourself a definite goal periodically and work toward that goal systematically.

This is what I expect of a college graduate in my particular vocation which happens to be medicine, but I think it applies to other vocations just as well. The technical requirements for admission are set by every medical school and can be found in the catalogue, but I think they are of secondary importance."

This was probably not the answer that was expected. I am far from underestimating the importance of factual knowledge. Without having acquired a solid scientific foundation you could not study medicine, but I think the primary task of a college is to develop in you the qualities and faculties that I have just mentioned.

Remember that all education is self-education. *You* must do the work; we cannot do it for you. *You* dissect, *you* handle the microscope, *you* observe patients, *you* must find out for yourself how things are. All we can do is help you in seeing them. We can teach you methods, can show you how to handle tools, but there are few short-cuts and I think the best we can do is to let you watch us and help us while we are at work, because like you we are learning all the time. We are all actively engaged in research; we are also trying to find out and are struggling against difficulties. We are thinking aloud for your benefit, and the fact that your teachers are students also will impress upon you that there is no such thing as a set body of knowledge that could simply be handed on to you. Science and learning are developing constantly, which means that you too will have to be students for life.

You will find the material presented to you during the next few years rather overwhelming unless you try to bring some order into it from the very beginning of your studies. Keep in mind that the foundation of all medical work is *observation* and *correct reasoning.* It would be a mistake to assume that laboratory tests have taken the place of observation. Before you can decide what tests you want to have made, you must have observed the patient, and the interpretation of an X-ray picture requires observation also. You must observe not only the patient but his environment. The more you have seen, the more factors you have in hand, the better you will be prepared to understand a sick man's condition and the more effectively you will be able to help him.

To observe things is not an easy matter, and many people go through life without being conscious of anything they see, taking it all for granted. Observation may well be practised not only at school but wherever you go. Riding in a crowded street-car, instead of being an ordeal, becomes a thrilling adventure if, taking advantage of the opportunity, you observe your fellow passengers. Watch their faces, the way they hold their hands, the way they are dressed; see what they read. By mere observation, without asking a single question, you will find out a great deal about them.

Never miss an opportunity to learn under what conditions people live and work. Whenever you have a chance, visit factories, farms, mines, the slums of your city and also the places where people seek rest and recreation. When you sail on a steamer try to see the engine room and the quarters of the crew. As a doctor you will have people from all walks of life call on you, and you cannot understand them nor help them effectively unless you are familiar with their mode of living.

In order to reason correctly in medicine you must have a solid knowledge of anatomy, physiology, psychology, and general pathology. In other words, you must acquire a three-dimensional view of the structure of the human body, you must know how the organs and the mind function normally and with what biological mechanisms they react against lesions. Do not spare any effort to acquire solid notions in these fields. Once you possess them you will find clinical medicine relatively easy to understand, but if you have only vague notions you will find yourselves entangled in an inextricable mesh of phenomena. Instead of understanding symptoms by relating them to their cause, you will try to memorize them, but you will soon find your memory failing you in view of the multiplicity of phenomena.

Throughout your studies remember always that our first goal is the promotion and preservation of health. I know that young medical students can hardly wait for the day when they will enter the hospital and will be in daily contact with sick people. The treatment of patients and the restoration of health are usually considered the major task of the physician. They are without any doubt extremely important, and without knowledge of diseases there is no way of preventing them. But every patient who comes to the hospital should be a reminder to us that medicine for some reason or other has failed to prevent this case of illness.

You must develop in yourself a positive attitude toward health, and must be interested not only in disease but in health and in its maintenance first of all. To that end you must yourself acquire sound health habits. It greatly weakens a physician's argument if he does not practise himself what he urges others to do, and a doctor who gets drunk is a disgrace to the profession. It is, of course, difficult to lead a normal hygienic life in these abnormal times when everyone is expected to do two men's work. But you simply must keep fit, and this requires that you organize your studies and your entire mode of living very systematically from the start.

*

You are entering medical school at a crucial moment of history, while the world is engaged in a desperate struggle. Conflicts that had been latent in every country for many years have become acute and have led to a world conflagration. It is now just twelve years since World War II broke out when Japanese troops occupied Mukden. To the superficial observer it looked as if the conflict could be localized in the Far East, but whoever had the faintest notion of history knew only too well that in a world like ours war as well as peace are indivisible. Events developed with iron logic. A few years later, in 1935, the war spread to Africa when fascist Italy invaded Ethiopia, and in 1936 the war had already reached the shores of Europe. The destruction of the Spanish republic by the combined action of the fascist powers with the consent of the democracies unleashed the floods definitely. Beginning in 1939 Poland, the Balkans, Western Europe and the Soviet Union were invaded, and in 1941 our own hemisphere found itself involved. The war was embracing the globe.

It would be futile to blame our statesmen for their lack of vision and courage. We must blame ourselves because our statesmen are the men that we have elected. They are the exponents of groups consisting of men and women like you and me. In order to prevent the war, they would have had to take actions that the people, uninformed as they were of the true nature of the conflict, would not have understood and would not have approved. But we must learn from past mistakes and this is where you, the young generation, have a tremendous responsibility. Your duty is to become not only good doctors but enlightened citizens.

I am sure you are aware of the fact that you are an extremely privileged group. At a time when most young men of your age are already in the fighting lines, scattered all over the world, you are permitted to spend a number of years at the university preparing for a profession that will serve the country and yourselves not only during but also after the war.

Most of you are in uniform today, and the people of the United States are paying for your tuition and are supporting you while you are studying. This is as it should be. The armed forces of the country need your services urgently and are therefore not asking whether you come from high-income or low-income families. They are taking a chance with you and are enabling all those who promise to become competent doctors to acquire the necessary knowledge and skills. Army discipline bears lightly on you so as not to interfere with the successful pursuit of your studies.

In return for all these privileges, the people of the United States may expect that you will make good use of the coming years, that you will work hard, planfully and intelligently, taking full advantage of the short time available. The time is very short indeed. Do not fool yourselves; the accelerated program is a real handicap. You may absorb all the courses offered but you will not be able to assimilate them as completely in three calendar years as you would in four, and you must be prepared to take a great deal of retraining after the war.

The fact that you are in uniform reminds you very strongly that you are not only individuals but members of a community which just now has mobilized you for its defense. The democratic community gives its members great rights, the greatest that can be extended, namely to determine its destinies. Rights, however, always imply obligations, and you who will have had the maximum of education and the best education that the country can give, will have the duty not only to serve the community as doctors but to serve it and to play a leading part in it as enlightened citizens.

Education in citizenship does not come by itself but requires hard work also. If you want to vote not only according to family tradition, not only emotionally as all too many people do, but intelligently, you must familiarize yourselves with the issues involved and study them thoroughly. You must learn to approach public matters in the same critical spirit in which you professionally approach problems of science. There is no more depressing sight than to see people praise or condemn a bill pending in Congress without even having taken the trouble to read it. It is strange how many physicians who are critical scientists in their profession, succumb to the most primitive type of propaganda and lose every critical sense as soon as social and economic issues are involved. In most cases, I am sure, this is due primarily to lack of education. But today, in a period of transition, you cannot afford to have such blind spots.

I know, of course, that the study of medicine is extremely absorbing, but you must find the time to read, to study, to debate among yourselves about the great social, economic, and political issues of the day. You cannot ignore them without punishment, because you yourselves as individuals have been thrown into the midst of them. They will determine your individual lives. The very fact that most of you are in uniform shows that these are unusual times. The world is aflame. Millions of people are dying. Why, what for? To-morrow's world will by necessity be very different from that of yesterday. Why? You will practise medicine under very different conditions than your fathers and grandfathers did. Why?

You must find an answer to these questions and the university will help you in finding it. You must know what we are fighting for, not "for my girl," not "to get it over with and go home"—the touching but naive answers of many of our soldiers. You as highly educated citizens must know that much greater issues are at stake, issues upon which the welfare not of one country but of mankind, and the very future of civilization depend.

And once the actual fighting is over you will have to take an active part in the reconstruction of the world. To-morrow's world will be that which you make it. You, the young generation, must raise your voice if you wish to prevent the old men, imbued in traditional views and prejudices, unwilling to recognize the changed conditions, from losing the peace as they did after the last war. Under the pressure of the emergency the army was forced to abandon old traditions and was forced to adopt new methods of warfare. It did it very effectively and in an amazingly short time. The emergency presented by the peace will be as great, and we must be as quick as the army was in adopting new views and methods required by the changed conditions.

There is another task which you as Hopkins students must bear in mind, the task of carrying on some day with medical research. After the war the ranks of our researchers will be badly depleted. A man who has been forced by circumstances to abandon his laboratory or study for a number of years very rarely finds the way back to it. Science develops very rapidly and once we have lost touch with it, it is extremely difficult to catch up. Thus there are bound to be many casualties on the research front, and you will have to fill the gaps.

*

I would like to address a special word to those of you who are not in uniform today, and to the young women who are entering our school with this class.

I know that it is awkward to be in civilian clothes in times of war when most other young men and many young women are in uniform. It will unavoidably happen that some people will look at you and wonder what is wrong with you. But, for goodness sake, do not let yourselves be discouraged. You are soldiers also, soldiers on the home front and in a total war the home front is equally important. Your studies are just as essential to the nation as those of your uniformed classmates, and you have to carry them out without the privileges granted to the others.

We all know that there is a great shortage of physicians in the war industries and in many sections of the country. Hospitals and all other health institutions are badly understaffed. The community is therefore eagerly waiting for your services. I think it is even fair to say that most young physicians in the armed forces have the easier lot. Their colleagues on the industrial front, in rural districts, in public health services are working day and night, struggling sometimes against great odds, sacrificing their health, with little compensation and without glamor and glory.

The young women in our midst I would like to remind that our school has admitted women on equal terms with men since its foundation, fifty years ago. The percentage of women represented in our classes is twice as large as the national percentage of women physicians. Even so it is small enough, but I am sure it will grow in the future in this country as it already has in others, as soon as medical services are properly organized, and also in view of the splendid record that women have already won in this war. The fact that after graduation you are now eligible for commissions in the medical corps of Army and Navy permits us to hope that the war will set an end to the ugly discrimination against women that was taking place not only in medicine but in every field and was a dark spot in our American civilization.

We have always welcomed you in this school, and you are doubly welcome to us today when your work is so urgently needed. Without the help of our women graduates it would be difficult to operate our departments.

*

I hope I have not frightened you by emphasizing the great responsibilities and obligations that you have assumed in entering our school at this crucial moment of history. Fifty years ago the world seemed stabilized, while today when we are beginning the second half century of our school, we find that everything is in motion and all values are revaluated.

But now let me end by pointing out the great joys that are in store for you. You are at the beginning of a great adventure. It is good to be young and to have one's life ahead, uncertain and difficult as it may turn out to be. It is a joy to be able to study medicine, for I cannot think of any more fascinating study. It combines the natural and the social sciences, combines intellectual and manual work. Its object is man—man in health and disease, in his physical and in his social environment. During the next few years you will be led through the heights and depths of human life. You will help young mothers in giving birth to new life. You will witness the agony of death, but also the rebirth of life in convalescence. And everywhere it will be given to you to help, in peace and even in war, to help in alleviating sufferings, to help in leading your fellow-men to a healthy and happy life. Truly, it is a great task, worthy of our highest efforts.

The *Institute of the History of Medicine* in which we find ourselves today, devotes its researches to the history, sociology, and economics of medicine. Through the method of historical and sociological analysis it endeavors to help you in understanding where we came from in medicine, at what point of the development we stand today, and into what direction we are moving. It wants you to look at medicine not as a technique but as a social function. It tries to prepare you for playing your part in society intelligently as physicians and citizens.

The *William H. Welch Medical Library* is the fifth largest medical library in the country, the largest university medical library, and probably the broadest library of its kind since it includes not only the collections of a great hospital, of a school of medicine and of a school of hygiene and public health, but also the rich historical collection of the Institute with all the background, source, and reference books needed for historical research. With this library the university is placing a first-rate tool into your hands that will greatly facilitate your studies.

Looking at you from the platform and seeing you so young and so eager, I almost envy you for the great experience that will be yours during the next few years. But I know that I will share it with you, and that I will relive my own student years by working with you and watching your development.

9

Classics of Medicine

A FEW YEARS ago I was sailing on a Black Sea steamer from Sochi to Yalta. There was a book kiosk on the boat, and it struck me that the books that were displayed most prominently and sold best, were biographies of great scientists and classics of science of which a new series was in course of publication. I watched an intelligent looking boy of about sixteen or perhaps seventeen years of age who browsed for a while and finally bought a volume that contained several treatises on electricity by Luigi Galvani and Alessandro Volta, in Russian translation.

The next morning, strolling on the deck I suddenly saw the young man, sitting on the floor, his forehead in both hands, deeply absorbed in reading his book. Desirous of making a test, I sat next to him and soon we were talking.

"How do you like this book?"

"It's fascinating, but very difficult."

"Why do you read such old stuff?"

He turned around sharply, looked me in the face and snapped out:

"I want to become an engineer. If I cannot understand what they knew a hundred and fifty years ago, how can I ever hope to understand what we must know today!"

I felt like kissing him on both cheeks, but he could not understand why I was rejoicing and probably thought that I was somewhat queer, as foreigners are.

Later, in Moscow, I tried to buy that series of classics of science for our library but could not find a single copy. I was told that the volumes were sold out within a few months, and that the shortage of paper unfortunately did not permit the printing of more than 10,000 copies of each at a time. It was only through the courtesy of a colleague who himself had translated and edited some of the volumes that I succeeded in obtaining several issues.

This experience made me think a great deal. I remembered how much Ostwald's *Klassiker der exakten Naturwissenschaften* had meant

Written in 1944.

[92]

to me in my college years. I had read dozens of them and had learned more from them than from textbooks. I find now that my copies are filled with pencil marks. Later, in medical school, I hardly ever left the house without having one of Sudhoff's *Klassiker der Medizin* in my pocket. I read them whenever there was a chance, in the streetcar, waiting for an appointment, and sometimes even in classes when the professor was dull. And I remember every one of them as if I had read them yesterday.

I also thought of the classics of medicine that our own Johns Hopkins Institute of the History of Medicine was publishing and of the pitiful response they had found.

*

When I took charge of the Hopkins Institute in 1932 I was looking for classics of medicine in English translation that could be used in seminary courses, but I found relatively little. There was Chauncey Leake's Harvey,[1] a book that should be in the hands of every medical student; there was Charles Singer's series which however never advanced beyond four volumes,[2] and the beautiful *Selected Readings* published by Charles C. Thomas,[3] and the anthology of John Ruhräh,[4]

[1] William Harvey, Exercitatio anatomica de motu cordis et sanguinis in animalibus. An English translation with annotations by Chauncey D. Leake. Springfield, Ill. and Baltimore, Md., Charles C Thomas, 1931.

[2] Lord Lister, Six papers; with a short biography and explanatory notes by Sir Rickman J. Godlee. London, J. Bale, Sons and Danielsson, Ltd., 1921.

John D. Comrie, Selected works of Thomas Sydenham. With a short biography and explanatory notes. London, J. Bale, Sons and Danielsson, Ltd.; New York, William Wood and Co., 1922.

Sir William Hale-White, Translation of Selected Passages from De l'Auscultation Médiate by R. Théophile H. Laennec. With a biography. London, John Bale, Sons and Danielsson, Ltd., 1923.

Dorothea Waley Singer, Selections from the works of Ambrose Paré. With short biography and explanatory and bibliographical notes. London, J. Bale, Sons and Danielsson, Ltd.; New York, William Wood and Co., 1924.

[3] Esmond R. Long, editor: Selected readings in pathology from Hippocrates to Virchow. Springfield, Ill. and Baltimore, Md., Charles C Thomas, 1929.

John Farquhar Fulton, editor: Selected readings in the history of physiology, Springfield, Ill. and Baltimore, Md., Charles C Thomas, 1930.

Ralph H. Major, Classic descriptions of disease, with biographical sketches of the authors. Springfield, Ill. and Baltimore, Md., Charles C Thomas, 1932.

[4] John Ruhräh, Pediatrics of the past. New York, Paul B. Hoeber, 1925. Later, two other valuable anthologies were published:

Frederick A. Willius and Thomas E. Keyes, Cardiac classics; a collection of classic works on the heart and circulation with comprehensive biographic accounts of the authors. St. Louis, The C. V. Mosby Co., 1941.

Logan Clendening, Source book of medical history. New York, Paul B. Hoeber, Inc., 1942.

books that make good reading but act more as appetizers because they do not reproduce entire treatises or papers but only select passages. In the field of ancient medicine Brock's *Greek Medicine* [5] was an extremely valuable source-book of which we made wide use, and a few volumes of the *Loeb Classical Library* [6] that contain medical texts were most welcome also.

Many medical classics, however, that we needed for our courses, were unavailable, and so we decided to launch our own series. Soon after we had started, Williams and Wilkins came out with a superb collection of classics, edited by Emerson C. Kelly, [7] and it became questionable whether we should continue with our own project. We decided to do so for various reasons. Kelly's collection is now complete in 5 volumes, each of which contains a number of classical texts and costs $10.00. The price puts the series beyond the reach of the average student. The individual texts, moreover, are not available separately so that a student who would like to possess Thomas Addison's *Effects of disease of the suprarenal capsules* would have to buy the whole volume. The great value of Ostwald's *Klassiker* lies just in the fact that every little volume contains one or a few related texts and can be bought for a few cents.

Kelly's collection, furthermore, includes mainly texts that are already available in English, [8] in other words, it does not enrich our medical literature. There is no doubt that every medical student should know some foreign languages, but actually very few master a language sufficiently to appreciate a text fully. Besides, many classics are written in Greek, Latin, Arabic, or in 15th or 16th century vernacular languages that are not easily understood. Translations then become interpretations and are imperative. There was not much need for reprinting Adams' translation of Hippocrates, as Kelly did, since it

---

[5] Arthur John Brock, editor. Greek medicine, being extracts illustrative of medical writers from Hippocrates to Galen. Translated and annotated. London and Toronto, J. M. Dent and Sons, Ltd.; New York, E. P. Dutton and Co., 1929.

[6] Galen, On the natural faculties. With an English translation by Arthur John Brock. London, W. Heinemann; New York, G. P. Putnam's Sons, 1916.

Hippocrates, with an English translation by W. H. S. Jones, London, W. Heinemann; New York, G. P. Putnam's Sons, 1923-1931. 4 vol.

Aulus Cornelius Celsus, De medicina. London, W. Heinemann; Cambridge, Mass., Harvard University Press, 1935-1938, 3 vol.

[7] Medical Classics, The Williams and Wilkins Co., Baltimore, Md., 5 vols., 1936-1941.

[8] With one conspicuous exception, Frank P. Murphy's translation of Semmelweis.

is probably available in most medical libraries in the edition of the Sydenham Society, and since the Loeb Classical Library includes better modern translations of the same writings. It would have been very desirable, however, to publish translations of the gynaecological and other "non-genuine" Hippocratic writings that are neither in Adams nor in the Loeb Library.[9]

Kelly's collection is extremely important and should be in as many hands as possible and certainly in every medical library where it should be fully analyzed and indexed in the catalogue. For the reasons just mentioned, however, we felt that there was still room for a series of classics and we went ahead with our project, slowly and somewhat haphazardly.

We had no special funds for the purpose and therefore published in the *Bulletin of the History of Medicine* whatever texts we needed or in which we were specially interested. And since we strongly felt that classics should not only be read but possessed, we had reprints made with special pagination, bound in boards, that could be sold for $.75 or $1.00.

This procedure had the advantage that it brought classics of medicine automatically to medical libraries and students of medical history who were subscribers to the *Bulletin,* and that it permitted publication of the volumes at little additional cost. It had the disadvantage that the format was rather large, while I would have preferred a pocket size for such texts, and, what was more serious, that it made us dependent on the space available. When the *Bulletin* became flooded with manuscripts, it was very difficult to include such texts and, as a result, we have issued only ten volumes so far.

In 1937 we launched an independent series of American medical classics. We thought that American physicians and students should be familiar with the development of medicine in their own country. Early American medical books are quite rare. They were printed in rather small editions and many copies were used up in the pioneer days. Our idea was to reprint some of the most significant medical texts with introductory essays and in this way to build up, in the course of time, a regular *Bibliotheca medica Americana* that physicians would

---

[9] I was informed by The Williams and Wilkins Company that they sold an average of 800 to 850 copies of the individual volumes of their series, but that they sold several thousand copies of Adams' translation of Hippocrates and that there is a continuous demand for it.

be glad to have on their shelves. The volumes were printed in an attractive format and type, but the series developed very slowly because funds were scanty and every volume involved a loss.

In 1941, commemorating the 400th anniversary of the death of Paracelsus, we published four Paracelsian treatises that illustrate four different aspects of his personality and work. The translations were the first ever attempted in English. They were made from the original 16th century German and presented considerable difficulties with regard to language and content. Each treatise was preceded by an introductory essay, and the whole volume was undoubtedly an interesting contribution to the history of Renaissance thought.

And so in the course of nine years we published 15 volumes of classics of medicine. We obviously never expected large sales. We published the books for the benefit of our students and of the English-speaking medical profession at large. The best we could expect financially was to recover the costs so that after an initial expenditure the money that came in could be used for the production of new volumes. It was, nevertheless, astonishing to see how little response our classics found. The following list will illustrate this best:

CLASSICS OF MEDICINE REPRINTED FROM BULLETIN OF THE HISTORY OF MEDICINE	Total number of copies sold to June 1, 1944
An Essay on the External Use of Water. By TOBIAS SMOLLETT. Edited with introduction and notes by Claude E. Jones, 1935. 54 pages, frontispiece, 8vo, $1.00	184
On Percussion of the Chest. By LEOPOLD AUENBRUGGER. Translated by John Forbes (1824). Introduction by Henry E. Sigerist. 1936. 31 pages, frontispiece, 8vo, 75 cents	314
A Dissertation on the Sensible and Irritable Parts of Animals. By ALBRECHT VON HALLER. 1755. Introduction by Owsei Temkin. 1936. 49 pages, frontispiece, 8vo, $1.00	79
Contributions to the Microscopic Anatomy of the Pancreas. By PAUL LANGERHANS. Reprint of the German original with an English translation and an introductory essay by H. Morrison. 1937. 39 pages, 1 plate, 8vo, $1.00	182
On Thought in Medicine. By HERMANN VON HELMHOLTZ. Introduction by Arno B. Luckhardt. 1938. 27 pages, frontispiece, 8vo, 75 cents	65

Classics of Medicine

Considering that there must be about 40,000 English-speaking
medical students and close to 250,000 English-speaking physicians in
the world, not counting scientists, dentists, pharmacists, veterinarians,
nurses, and members of other allied professions, and considering that
there are 315 medical libraries in the United States alone, the sale of
our classics can certainly not be called staggering. And this raises the
question: Why should such books be published at all? Why should
anybody read them? Did the Russian boy on the Black Sea steamer
in his spontaneous way answer the question?

*

Medical writings, books and papers, become out-dated very
rapidly, the sooner the more rapidly medical science progresses. In
static periods such as the Middle Ages medical information was
sought from books that had been written many centuries before, while
today a book in order to be kept alive must be revised and published
in a new edition every few years. It usually dies with its author, and
its place is taken over by a new book written by a new man. The
overwhelming majority of all medical writings fall into oblivion after
less than twenty-five years and are read or consulted by historians
alone.

This is true not only of medical, but also of other books. Most
"best-sellers" of today, selections of the Book-of-the-Month Club, are
dead after a few years, and some day in the future students will write
dissertations trying to find out why a particular book appealed at
a given time to large sections of the half-educated middle class.

But there are exceptions. There are books, medical books also,
that do not die. They continue to be printed in new editions, are

read by generation after generation, and gradually become part of our classical literature.

It is relatively easy to understand how a novel, drama or poem may become classical, but things are different in medicine. Science progresses every day. The truth of today is the untruth of tomorrow. By what mechanism does a medical book or paper survive the test of time?

Here it seems to me that we must distinguish between different types of medical classics. Claude Bernard's *Introduction à l'étude de la médecine expérimentale,* first published in 1865, can still be seen in Paris in windows of medical bookstores. After eighty years, during which medicine made gigantic advances, the book is still bought and read by thoughtful students. Why? Because the experimental method which in the hands of Claude Bernard yielded such brilliant results, is still our chief method of research today so that his book is still fully alive. This is true of his other writings. Most of his discoveries have been generally accepted and have become part of the body of our physiological knowledge. A student can simply learn from a textbook that carbohydrates are stored in the liver as glycogen and can take it for granted. But if he takes the trouble to find out by what reasoning and through which experiments Claude Bernard made this great discovery, he will not only understand the facts much better but will at the same time learn how knowledge is obtained.

The most difficult task of medical education is teaching the students to think—to think in terms of biology and, I may add, also in terms of sociology. It is easy to teach facts, but difficult to teach correct reasoning by which the facts are correlated. Brought face to face with a patient, the student's task is to reconstruct a segment from a man's life. Through questioning and observation he must find what kind of an individual the patient is, physically, mentally and socially, how he lived and what happened to him up to the time that brought him to the doctor. The examination will reveal symptoms, and the student with all these facts in hand, will then reconstruct and evaluate the biological process that is taking place in the patient whereupon it becomes possible to prescribe a treatment.

Every teacher of medicine teaches how to think, if not explicitly in words, then through his example, but the student can in addition learn a great deal from the great masters of the past. Classical descriptions of disease like those collected in Ralph Major's inspiring book are unsurpassed masterpieces of medical observation and reasoning. The young student who struggles to hear sounds when practising percussion may feel greatly helped by reading the simple presentation of Auenbrugger who invented the method. Who could talk more competently *On Thought in Medicine* than Helmholtz? Arthus' *Philosophy of Scientific Investigation* is an address that every young researcher will read with great benefit, and Henle's treatise *On Miasmata and Contagia* is a superb example of sound biological thinking. Anticipating the germ-theory of disease, long before Pasteur's and Koch's discoveries, he came to the conclusion that miasmata and contagia must be identical and must be animated. Pettenkofer's two lectures on *The Value of Health to a City* are as forceful and persuasive today as they were in 1873 when he delivered them to a Munich audience, and it was very gratifying to hear that the translation we recently published, stimulated several South African public health officers to calculate the value of health to their communities exactly as Pettenkofer did for Munich.

Not every physician will become a researcher, but as a student every doctor has spent a number of years at the very source of medical research, in daily contact with a group of men who have devoted their life to the advancement of science, who have permitted him to enter their sanctum, to breath its atmosphere and to share the joys and sorrows of the researcher. This is a great privilege that imposes upon every medical man the obligation to keep in close touch with science and to make his experience available for the advancement of medicine. Could there be any more inspiring example than Withering's treatise on the foxglove, or Jenner's treatise on vaccination, or Robert Koch's paper on anthrax? They demonstrate what great and lasting contributions the practitioner can make.

It would be a mistake to believe that research can be carried out only in lavishly equipped institutions. Certain investigations obviously require very elaborate instruments and apparatuses and all the resources of a hospital, but the practitioner working up his cases, with the modest means available to him can without any doubt make important contributions. He sees cases that never come to a hospital, and I should think that such subjects as heredity, human constitution, psychological behavior, social etiology, to mention only a few, present a wide field of investigation to the practitioner. The German pioneer of modern social medicine, A. Grotjahn, gathered his rich experience as a general practitioner. The great Swiss ophthalmologist Alfred Vogt did some very important work while he was a small-town practitioner. There are many classics of medicine that demonstrate this point unmistakably. The doctor who takes them along when he enters practice and keeps them on his shelves, will find them a constant source of inspiration.

How often have we not wished that we could have lived at the time of Claude Bernard, of Pasteur or Osler, that we could have been their students, could have listened to their teachings. We can be their students today. They are not dead. They talk to us through their writings. By reading their books, papers or addresses we enlarge the circle of our teachers immeasurably. The greatest minds of medicine enter our classroom and admit us to their clinics and to their laboratories. Textbooks grow out of date because they give a cross-section through the knowledge that a period has of a given field. Original as they may be, they necessarily always have a certain compilatory character. But monographs, the papers in which a researcher describes his new findings, or writings such as the immortal essays of Osler in which he expounded his philosophy of life and his philosophy of medicine—they remain young, appeal to us immediately and bring us in close touch with the minds that created them.

There is another aspect to the matter. Students in the course of their studies have to learn many very difficult and complicated subjects. The historical approach is undoubtedly one that greatly helps us in understanding difficult problems. As a student in high school I was a very poor mathematician until I began to study the history of mathematics. Then all of a sudden things were clear, I understood them. Goethe was certainly right when he said: *Die Geschichte der Wissenschaft ist die Wissenschaft selbst.* And the Russian boy on the Black Sea steamer was correct when he felt that once we have mastered the knowledge of the past we are better prepared to assimilate the more complex knowledge of our day. The reading of medical classics, therefore, is not only a source of inspiration, not only teaches us to think, but is also a very good method of acquiring factual knowledge.

Facts are brought to us in a much more impressive way through the original writings of the men who discovered them than through textbooks. In Gray's Anatomy the parathyroid glands are described on two pages in a sequence of matter-of-fact sentences. The description of their anatomy begins:

The parathyroid glands are small brownish-red bodies, situated as a rule between the posterior borders of the lateral lobes of the thyroid gland and its capsule. They differ from it in structure, being composed of masses of cells arranged in a more or less columnar fashion with numerous intervening capillaries. . . .

Ivar Sandström of Upsala who discovered the glands in 1877 and described them in 1880 begins his paper thus:

About three years ago I found on the thyroid gland of a dog a small organ, hardly as big as a hemp seed, which was enclosed in the same connective tissue capsule as the thyroid, but could be distinguished therefrom by a lighter color. A superficial examination revealed an organ of a totally different structure from that of the thyroid and with a very rich vascularity. . . .

Those two words, *I found,* make the whole difference in the world, and in describing the new glands Sandström gives a colorful report of a personal experience. A modern textbook obviously conveys more information on the subject because it summarizes all the work done on the subject from 1880 on, but a student who in addition to using a textbook reads some of the basic original papers will understand and remember the facts much better.

There is, finally, another group of classics of medicine that we reprint and read for somewhat different reasons. We translate and publish works of Greek, Mediaeval, Renaissance, 17th and 18th century physicians because they are great historical and cultural documents, stepping stones in the development of medicine. We make them available because we believe that the physician should be an educated man and not a mere technician. He should have some knowledge of the history of civilization, and where could he find a better introduction into the subject than in the history of his own craft and science? Not every doctor can appreciate Plato, but he will immediately feel at home when he reads a Hippocratic writing because he is familiar with the subject matter. Ambroise Paré's treatise on gunshot wounds of 1545 does not teach us how to treat war wounds today, because surgery has greatly advanced in four hundred years and methods of warfare have changed, but it is a great document of the history of surgery, which revolutionized the treatment of gunshot wounds at the time. It illustrates an aspect of life in the Renaissance, and through it we become acquainted with an interesting and most lovable character of the period.

We know much more about syphilis and typhus than Girolamo Fracastoro did, but his treatise on contagious diseases of 1546 has become a classic for the correctness of the observations and the soundness of the reasoning it contains. Like Paré's treatise, it also illustrates an important aspect of the period, and the same is true for the works of Paracelsus, Vesalius and many other medical writers.

The earlier classics of medicine appeal not only to medical readers. The Hippocratic writings are just as important to the history of philosophy as to the history of medicine, and whoever studies Greek civilization in the classical period cannot ignore them. Bernardino Ramazzini's treatise on the diseases of craftsmen of 1700 is not only the great classic of industrial medicine, but an extremely important source to the history of labor conditions. In the same way Benjamin W. McCready's essay *On the Influence of Trades, Professions and Occupations, in the United States in the Production of Disease* of 1837, recently published by our Institute, is far more than a medical document. Written by a young doctor who had not much medical experience in the field, it nevertheless gives a very good picture of living and labor conditions in this country and particularly in New York, one hundred years ago. McCready's dissertation was not a contribution to world medicine, but it deserved being reprinted as a source to the history of American civilization,[10] just as we reprinted Thomas Thacher's broadside on small pox of 1677 because it was the first medical text printed in this country, or John Morgan's *Discourse upon the Institution of Medical Schools in America* of 1765, because it marked the beginning of our first medical school.

In spite of the fact that we already have a number of medical classics available, I think there is still room for another more comprehensive and more systematic series of classics, and if somebody should

[10] See in this connection: Richard H. Shryock, The need for studies in the history of American science, *Isis*, 1944, 35: 10-13.

happen to give me $10,000 I know how I would spend them. I would consult with my colleagues and would find out from them which original articles they thought students attending their courses should read, in addition to using textbooks. I would reprint these articles, would have them translated if necessary, and would publish them, each one separately, or related ones together, in booklets of pocket-size, beautifully printed as becomes such texts, each one with a brief introduction pointing out the significance of the article and the place it takes in the field and in its general development. Thus one section of the series would be devoted to anatomy, others to physiology, biochemistry, pathology, etc. until the basic texts were made easily available for each subject of medical instruction. The articles chosen need not be old. Recent important papers—classics of tomorrow—that every student should read could be included in the series. There is a great difference between reading a paper at the library and possessing it. In the course of time other sections could be added intended primarily for practitioners, for historians, or for students of the humanities and social sciences.

The individual booklets should not cost more than $.25, less than two packs of cigarettes. They should be on sale at the library, in the departments, at the student bookstore, at the corner drug store, wherever students go in the course of the day. Thus it would become possible gradually to build up a kind of "Modern Library" of medicine which, I have no doubt, would enrich medical education and would be a source of inspiration to all groups of the medical profession and to others.

Since it is very unlikely that anybody will give me $10,000 for such a purpose, I will continue to recommend whatever classics we have available today and our Institute will continue to publish a few texts from time to time whenever conditions permit it.

*

Reading over what I have written, I am disturbed to find that my article sounds very much like a sales talk, as if I were trying to "boost" the sale of our Institute classics. I need not tell that our department has no financial stake in these books. They are produced at little cost and returns, while not unwelcome, are hardly expected.

Of course, we would like to see these books widely read, but sales will not influence our policy. If we never sold more than five copies we would still continue to publish classics because they must be available, and because the few copies sold may exert a decisive influence on a few students who may become the medical leaders of to-morrow.

10

Trends in Medical Education

A PROGRAM FOR A NEW MEDICAL SCHOOL

THE PRESENT paper owes its origin to a seminar course on the development·of social medicine held at the Johns Hopkins Institute of the History of Medicine during the academic year 1939-1940. The course was attended by students of the School of Medicine and of the School of Hygiene and Public Health. After having discussed the changes that have occurred in medicine and society and the growing need for social medicine, the students became very critical of our present system of medical education, pointing out that it hardly took these new developments into account. We then set ourselves the task to draw up a plan for a new medical school that would train the physician that to-morrow's society will require.

The present paper was not written for publication but for the benefit of the students as a summary of our seminar discussion. Only a few mimeographed copies were sent outside the Institute to colleagues whom we knew to be particularly interested in the subject. Somehow, the paper became known and there were so many requests for copies that I finally decided to publish it in the *Bulletin of the History of Medicine*.[1] Once it was published the demand for reprints was such that the supply of 750 copies was exhausted in a very short time. The paper also attracted a good deal of attention abroad. It was reproduced by the Health Survey and Development Committee of the Government of India for the use of its members and was discussed in other sections of the British Empire.

The unexpected reception of this paper showed that our seminar had touched upon a subject of vital importance. I am, therefore, including it into this collection in spite of its sketchy character.

[1] 1941, 9: 177-198.

Trends in Medical Education

I. The Need

1.

Education always presupposes an educational ideal. General education has an ideal citizen in mind, and the purpose of the schools is to produce this ideal citizen or at least to train young people toward that goal and to bring them as close to the ideal as possible.

Similarly, medical education has an ideal physician in mind. Schools and curricula are organized in such a way that their end product will be a physician who conforms with the ideal or comes as close to it as possible.

It is important to know that the medical ideal has changed a great deal in course of time and is evolving constantly. As a result, medical education can never reach definite forms but is obliged to adapt itself to changing conditions. Every society required of its physician that he have knowledge, skill, devotion to his patients and similar qualities. But the position of the physician in society, the tasks assigned to him and the rules of conduct imposed upon him by society changed in every period. The physician was a priest in Babylonia, a craftsman in ancient Greece, a cleric in the early and a scholar in the later Middle Ages. He became a scientist with the rise of the natural sciences, and it is perfectly obvious that the requirements put upon the physician and the tasks of medical education were different in all these periods.

We must keep in mind that the picture a society has of its ideal doctor—the goal of medical education—is determined primarily by two factors: the social and economic structure of that society and the technical means available to medical science at that time.

When the medical ideal is clearly defined and conscious in the people's minds, medical education adapts itself and reaches for a while more or less stable forms. In periods of transition, however, when social and economic conditions change rapidly, when the medical ideal is not clearly recognized, or when different generations have different ideals, there is by necessity unrest in medical education. The majority of educators, conservative by nature, may remain convinced of the excellence of existing institutions, while others will feel critical and will seek new forms, a system that will train not the physician of yesterday but the physician of to-morrow. At such a moment the time has come for clear analysis of the situation and for courageous experimentation.

2.

In the first half of the 19th century the American physician was a family doctor. The structure of the society he was called to serve was infinitely simpler than today. Only one out of five gainfully employed persons was a wage-earner or salaried employee, while four were independent farmers, craftsmen or business men. Medical science was still undeveloped technically. The physician was trained on a more or less empirical basis with a very thin theoretical foundation. The length of studies was short and the physician could begin to practise with simple and inexpensive equipment. As a result of all these factors the cost of medical care was relatively low and large sections of the population could afford to purchase medical services. The doctor succeeded in making a decent living by serving a number of families regularly. Fee schedules allowed him to apply the sliding scale and he gave his services free of charge to indigents who called on him, or in hospitals with which he was connected. Hospitals were few, simple in equipment and serving the indigent population.

At the time of the Civil War medical conditions were chaotic. The rapid expansion of the country and the pressing demand for more physicians had led to the foundation of a large number of proprietary medical schools which were neither physically nor intellectually prepared to train competent physicians.

A gradual readjustment took place after the War. Since the schools could not be trusted, the States required a license for practice which was granted after successful examination given by a State Board of Medical Examiners. Medical Societies founded in increasing numbers endeavored to improve conditions of education and practice. In 1889 the Johns Hopkins Hospital and in 1893 the Johns Hopkins School of Medicine were opened in Baltimore. A new departure was made in American medical education.

3.

In the 50 years preceding the opening of the Johns Hopkins Medical School medical science had made great progress. Improved microscopes made the investigation of cellular structures possible. Physiology was revolutionized by the progress of physics, particularly of electricity and optics and by the tremendous development of organic chemistry. This new physiology was creating a new experimental pharmacology and a new scientific hygiene. Pathological anatomy had become cellular pathology and this new principle applied to a study of diseases of skin, eyes, ear and other organs created new disciplines. Bacteriology was beginning its triumphant way and revolutionized public health and surgery. A new clinic developed which was based on clinical observation, pathology and the laboratory.

The task of medical education around 1890 was to train a physician who would still primarily be a family doctor, to be sure, but who would be a scientific physician fully equipped with all means of medical science and prepared to cooperate with the hospital which was also changing its character basically. It was no longer merely a place for the treatment of indigent patients, but was now sought by all groups of the population for examinations, treatments and for childbirth.

The men who founded the Johns Hopkins Medical School took over elements of the various European systems of medical education and succeeded in blending them into a new system which proved to be very satisfactory. The basic principles of this system can be summarized as follows:

1. The requirements for admission were raised. Only those students were admitted who had completed a full college course including prescribed courses in biology, physics and chemistry and who had a working knowledge of Latin, German and French. Medical education became graduate education.

2. Lectures which so burdened the German curriculum were reduced to a minimum and replaced by seminars and practical courses.

3. All instruction was given by men actively engaged in research in their respective fields.

4. The medical course was 4 years. The first two years were devoted to laying a solid foundation in the basic sciences. Most instruction took place in laboratories. The second two years were devoted to clinical instruction in hospital wards, dispensaries and clinical laboratories.

5. The system of spoon feeding with its quizzes and tests still customary in the schools was abolished. The students were treated as adults and given great freedom in organizing their studies and supplementing required by elective courses.

Internship in a hospital after completion of the medical course was not required but encouraged, and practically all graduates spent one or more years in hospital work. An internship of one year later became a requirement for the state board examination of a number of states.

The Johns Hopkins School of Medicine set an example that was followed by other schools in the ensuing decades. The wise and energetic policy of Abraham Flexner and of the General Education Board and the standardizing influence of the American Medical Association and the American Association of Medical Colleges wiped out inferior schools and compelled others to reorganize from the very bottom. This process, slow in the beginning, was accelerated after World War I and today the country has 10 two-year schools of medical sciences giving adequate instruction in the basic sciences and 66 four-year schools training scientific physicians.

In Europe medical faculties of the universities admit all students seeking admission provided they can satisfy the entrance requirements. If the number of students increases, the university is obliged to increase its educational facilities, or, at least, is supposed to do so, which is not always the case. In the United States the tendency was, and still is, to limit the number of students according to facilities available. The present schools admit from 50 to 180 students every year. While there undoubtedly are advantages in having a small, carefully selected body of students instructed in small groups by a large faculty, the system has led to serious discriminations, and has provided an easy pretext for racial and other prejudices.

Colored students are refused admittance in all southern schools— and in this respect the South extends very far north. They are segregated into two colored schools (Howard, Meharry) and only very few of them are admitted incidentally to northern schools where their position is far from enviable. The high tuition fees exclude them automatically from many northern schools. Jewish students are subject to a tacit, but nevertheless highly effective, quota-system and in most schools the number of Jewish students admitted rarely exceeds

10 per cent of the total enrolment. Discrimination is also applied against women, whereby the idea is that women are not a safe investment since they may marry and not exercise their profession.

4.

Is there any need for a reorganization of medical studies? In order to answer the question we must raise another: Have conditions changed in the last 50 years? Will the society of to-morrow require a different type of physician than that of yesterday?

The changes have been tremendous indeed. Medical science has progressed still further and has become still more technical and still more specialized. A highly developed physiology using complicated methods of chemistry and physics has become the backbone of every medical field. The discovery of hormones and vitamins has opened up new horizons. New diagnostic methods such as the application of X-rays and the electrocardiograph allow a sharp analysis of a patient's condition. New methods of treatment have made it possible to cure diseases that were deadly only yesterday. Public health no longer limits its field to the traditional tasks of quarantine and sanitation. It has moved closer to the individual and has established services for the care of pregnant women, infants, school children and for the combating of venereal diseases, tuberculosis and industrial diseases.

As a result of these developments the incidence of illness has changed completely. Acute diseases are no longer in the foreground but the chronic diseases of mature and old age, those diseases that require close and steady supervision by the physician.

Medical science is sufficiently advanced today to give the physician the scientific means necessary in order to practise preventive medicine on a large scale. Prevention of disease must be in every physician's mind whatever his position may be.

In the last 50 years the scope of medicine has broadened considerably. The doctor is no longer the mere therapist that he used to be. He has become the adviser of the educator. Mental hygiene, in its infancy still, will become the chief method in keeping developing individuals socially adjusted, the chief weapon in the prevention of crime.

The doctor has become the scientific and psychological adviser to the court. The administration of the law would be impossible without him. He determines the cause of death and the circumstances under which death occurred. He determines the responsibility of the defendant, and more and more often he is called upon by the judge to advise him in determining a sentence that will not punish but rehabilitate and readjust an unsocial individual to his environment.

The physician is also increasingly becoming the adviser to the statesman. The chief cause of disease still is poverty with all its dire consequences—slums, malnutrition, prostitution, alcoholism, and crime. The solution of these problems is not medical but political. The physician, however, who is in close touch with the people, who daily sees the evil effects of poverty for the individual and for society, has an important task to fulfill. He knows the conditions—conditions that are often not mentioned aloud so as not to disturb the people's minds. He can draw the attention of his fellow-citizens to these conditions, can tell them what slums mean, not only to their inhabitants but to the community at large. He can contribute to keep the conscience of society awake, can advise the statesman technically, and as a citizen can assume leadership in improving conditions.

The progress of medicine necessarily increased the cost of medical care so much that today large sections of the population are unable to purchase the medical services they need. Philanthropic institutions can not possibly satisfy the demand. And while the development of science and technology led to great medical progress, the same factors effected basic changes in the structure of society. When electricity was introduced into industry around 1900, a second industrial revolution took place and we find ourselves today in a highly industrialized, highly specialized and differentiated society in which four out of every five gainfully employed persons are wage-earners or salaried employees. In a society in which four-fifths of all bread-winners depend for a living on the labor market, have a job today but may lose it to-morrow, there is obviously a strong feeling of insecurity and, as a consequence, a strong demand for social security in health matters.

There can be no doubt that adjustments will be made in the distribution of medical care in a very near future. We do not know yet whether this will be effected through an extension of public services, voluntary or compulsory insurance or a combination of all, but one thing is certain, that the physician of to-morrow will practise medicine under different conditions than in the past.

5.

From all that has been said it becomes apparent that great changes have indeed occurred in the last fifty years in medicine and in society, and whoever is aware of developments cannot doubt that a new type of physician is needed.

We still need, more than ever, a scientific physician, well-trained in laboratory and clinic. But we need more: we need a social physician who, conscious of developments, conscious of the social functions of medicine, considers himself in the service of society.

There is no point in training doctors primarily for city practice among the upper middle class. The overwhelming majority of all patients consists of people of very moderate means, of indigents and poor negroes. At the point of development at which we stand, we must still count with the possibility of unemployment once the war boom has come to an end. The average student, while he is in medical school, hopes for a lucrative practice that will allow him to give services of high quality, applying all the scientific devices with which he becomes familiar during the course. Very few ever get such a practice. The majority of all young physicians soon realize that they cannot apply much of what they have learned. Patients are too poor to pay for the examinations or treatments they need, or adequate hospital facilities are unavailable. The scientific standard of the young doctor soon drops, particularly under the pressure of sometimes strong competition. He develops a routine. Unable to collect many of his bills, he becomes dissatisfied.

We must train our students in the idea that they will have to serve first of all the low-income groups who need their services most. We must make them familiar with their problems, their living and working conditions. We must show them the best that can be done under existing conditions and must impress upon them that medicine is not competitive business but a service, that there is no direct relation between their work and their income. All they can hope for materially is to make a decent though modest living, but the compensations are endless.

The general practitioner will remain the core of the medical profession, but alone, left to himself, he is lost and cannot possibly practise scientific medicine. He needs the backing of a health centre or hospital and a group of specialists whose help and advice he can seek. In other words: practice tomorrow will by necessity be group practice, organized around a health centre. This was already recommended in 1932 by the Committee on the Costs of Medical Care, and whatever plans of medical organization may be adopted in the future, they must ultimately accept the principle of group practice since this is the most efficient form of medical service. It is important therefore to train students from the beginning in teamwork and in a spirit of cooperation.

Medicine must become preventive medicine. To quote Sir George Newman, "The ideal of medicine is the prevention of disease, and the necessity for curative treatment is a tacit admission of its failure."

The barriers between preventive and curative medicine must be broken down. This cannot be achieved by adding a few courses to the curriculum. A new attitude must be developed. The student must become interested in health, not only in disease. Clinical medicine must be taught differently than heretofore. Every case must be analyzed medically and socially as to the factors that have made it possible, and conclusions must be drawn how to prevent similar cases in the future.

Since the physician will have to cooperate very closely with public health officers he must be familiar with the elementary tasks of public health.

And so we actually begin to see the outlines of a new physician. Scientist and social worker, ready to cooperate in teamwork, in close touch with the people he disinterestedly serves, a friend and leader, he directs all his efforts toward the prevention of disease and becomes a therapist where prevention has broken down—the social physician protecting the people and guiding them to a healthier and happier life.

6.

We now must raise the question whether the existing medical schools of the country are aware of this new ideal and have adjusted themselves to the changed conditions. The answer is definitely: no.

There is no doubt that American medical education has greatly progressed technically. Scientific standards are as a rule high. New courses have been added to the curriculum to include new subjects. But basically the curriculum has not changed. Spirit and objective remain the same. As in the past students are trained in the technology and not in the sociology of medicine.

It is interesting to study in this respect the latest document published by the American Medical Association, *Medical Education in the United States, 1934-1939.* The words society, sociology, economics, history do not occur in the index. Interesting experiments undertaken in various schools to broaden the scope of medical education are not even mentioned. Nobody reading the report could possibly find that it was written in 1939.

Once we recognize that conditions of medicine and society have changed and that a new type of physician is needed we must admit that the objective of medical education has changed also. A new medical school with a new curriculum to make a new step forward in the training of physicians is needed today as it was 50 years ago when the Johns Hopkins School of Medicine was organized.

II. Principles

1. The School shall be open to qualified students irrespective of race, creed or sex.
2. Requirement for admission shall be the successful completion of a two-year course in a College of Arts and Science of recognized standard, or its equivalent.
3. The medical course shall be based upon a curriculum of six years' duration.

About 50 per cent of all students entering medical schools have a bachelor's degree and the tendency of the better schools is to require the completion of a college course of 4 years. The traditional medical course of 4 years, however, is too short for adequate training and it seems advisable therefore to work the 2 senior college years into the medical curriculum. This allows a much better integrated program. Departments of physics, chemistry and biology, moreover, are valuable assets to a medical school in its research work.

4. The Degree of Bachelor of Science shall be conferred upon students after successful completion of the first two years of the course and presentation of an acceptable essay.
5. The Degree of Doctor of Medicine shall be conferred upon students after successful completion of the full six-years' course and presentation of an acceptable dissertation.

While most European universities require an inaugural-dissertation for the doctor's degree American universities do not. Yet it cannot be denied that the educational value of the preparation of a dissertation is tremendous. It teaches a student methods of research and trains him in presenting a scientific subject adequately. It reminds him that his duty later as a practitioner will be to contribute to the advancement of medicine by making important observations known. To the departments of the School the student dissertations offer a welcome opportunity to have a good deal of accessory research done and materials published.

6. Postgraduate education is becoming increasingly needed and the School should foresee the establishment of various types of postgraduate courses such as: 1. Short courses of a few weeks on a specific subject; 2. Courses of several months on a broader subject and possibly 3. An all-round one-year course.

7. The training of auxiliary medical personnel (clinical nurses, public health nurses, midwives, medical social workers, laboratory technicians, etc.) is just as important as the training of physicians and needs just as much reorganization along new lines. The School should foresee a special division for the training of such personnel, closely integrated with the curriculum of the medical student. Students of medicine must learn from the very beginning to work in teams with the auxiliary personnel.

8. The tuition fees should be kept as low as ever possible and scholarships should be available for all groups of students.

9. Students must learn to practise preventive medicine on themselves. The School should foresee a *Medical Service* to provide entrance and periodic examinations as well as treatments to all people employed in the School (faculty, students and employees).

III. The Medical Course

A. General Remarks

1. Education is self-education. Purpose of the curriculum is to guide the student and to help him in developing his personality and a correct attitude toward the problems of health, and in acquiring knowledge and skills in the technology and sociology of medicine.

2. The student shall be in touch with the sick man from the first year on.

The young student entering school is most eager to get in touch with patients and yet under the present system he must wait years before he sees a sick man. There is no doubt that a solid scientific foundation is necessary for clinical work, but by doing some nursing and medical social work and by assisting physicians in the dispensaries the student will acquire valuable experiences particularly in practical psychology. Such work, moreover, will give added meaning to his theoretical studies.

3. The academic year shall be 8 months or 30 weeks and shall be divided in 2 semesters of 15 weeks each. In order to prevent the curriculum from becoming rigid, not more than ¾ of the time available shall be devoted to required courses. The student shall have ¼ of the time available for independent work and for attending elective courses.

Time available for Instruction

	Total Number of hours	Required	Free and Elective
Year	1200	900	300
Semester	600	450	150
Week	40	30	10

4. Instruction shall consist of lectures, seminars, conferences, demonstrations, excursions, practical work in laboratories and hospitals, field work, and student activities.

5. Required courses shall be supplemented by elective courses offered by all divisions and departments whereby special attention will be given to joint seminars of the various divisions for the study of such problems as: Rural Health, Health Problems of the Negro Population, etc.

6. The academic course shall be supplemented by 2 months of field work every summer. See page 121.

B. The Course Year by Year

Only required courses have been listed and the number of hours indicated for each course is a mere suggestion intended to show that such a curriculum is possible. It is obviously not the number of hours that counts but the quality of instruction. Subjects have been listed under their general heading and will have to be subdivided, for instance, anatomy into gross anatomy, histology and neurology. A subject like physical therapy has not been listed especially, but will be taught under medicine and surgery. The distribution of courses over the 2 semesters, their sequence and integration will have to be worked out. Methods of instruction have not been discussed since this would require a paper in itself. The purpose of the following list is merely to indicate in a summary way the chief subjects to be included in the curriculum whereby the traditional headings have been preserved for the sake of brevity.

I. First Year

	HOURS
1. Introduction to Medicine	30
2. History of Science	30
3. Philosophy	15
4. Languages and Literature	60
5. Mathematics	30
6. Physics	200
7. Chemistry	205
8. Biology	240
9. Nursing, Medical Social Work, Dispensary Work	90
Total	900

II. Second Year

	HOURS
1. History of Medicine	30
2. Anthropology (Physical and Social)	30
3. Psychobiology	30
4. Languages and Literature	60
5. Biostatistics	30
6. Chemistry	210
7. Anatomy	210

8. Physiology and Physiological Chemistry . . 210
9. Nursing, Medical Social Work, Dispensary
Work 90

Total 900

III. Third Year

                                                    HOURS
1. Sociology of Medicine 30
2. Anatomy 210
3. Physiology and Physiological Chemistry . . 210
4. Pathology 175
5. Bacteriology 75
6. Epidemiology 30
7. Psychopathology 30
8. Prevention, Diagnosis, and Treatment of Diseases [1] 140

Total 900

IV. Fourth Year

                                                    HOURS
1. Economics of Medicine 30
2. Pathology 150
3. Pharmacology 75
4. Nutrition, Housing, Sanitation 45
5. Medicine [2] 175
6. Surgery [2] 175
7. Obstetrics–Gynecology 130
8. Pediatrics 75
9. Psychiatry (Psychoses) 45

Total 900

[1] An introductory clinical course given jointly by all clinical professors. The purpose of the course is to train the students in the observation of disease symptoms and
in clinical thinking. The unity of medicine will be stressed so that the student realizes
that medicine does not consist of specialties, but that pathological processes are basically
the same in all organs and that only the methods of diagnosis and treatment are
specialized.

[2] Time will be taken off for instruction in physical and laboratory diagnostics.

V. Fifth Year

		HOURS
1. Social Medicine		30
2. Medicine		175
3. Dermatology		45
4. Surgery		175
5. Ophthalmology		75
6. Oto-Rhino-Laryngology		50
7. Radiology		45
8. Pediatrics, Including Infant Welfare and School Hygiene		75
9. Obstetrics–Gynecology, Including Theory and Practice of Birth Control		125
10. Psychiatry (Neuroses)		45
11. Clinical-Pathological Conference		30
12. Medico-Sociological Conference		30
Total		900

VI. Sixth Year

		HOURS
1. The Physician in Society		15
2. Public Health Administration		15
3. Medicine		175
4. Neurology		60
5. Surgery		160
6. Orthopedics		30
7. Urology		30
8. Stomatology		30
9. Tuberculosis, Clinical and Social		60
10. Venereal Diseases, Clinical and Social		70
11. Industrial Hygiene, Occupational Diseases, Workmen's Compensation		60
12. Physical Education, Rest and Recreation		30
13. Forensic Medicine		60
14. Mental Hygiene		45

[120]

VII. Field Work

The academic course shall be supplemented by two months of field work every summer.

Teams consisting of students of medicine, nursing, midwifery, student-technicians, etc. shall be sent out with or without instructors according to the task. Such teams could serve a very useful purpose in a great variety of fields. All government health services, municipal, state and federal are understaffed as a rule and could make good use of additional workers during the four summer months. The students thus could work in clinics, nurseries, rural health centres, on Indian reservations, in migrant agricultural workers' camps, in distressed areas of the south. They could be used for special purposes such as immunization campaigns, health education, the making of chest X-rays of large groups, surveys of various kinds. There is no doubt that in the future the Government will establish an increasing number of rural health centres and the School could contract with the Government to staff and operate such centres. It would improve the services and would provide the School with centres of research and instruction in different sections of the country.

A plan would be worked out according to which the student during the course of five summers would obtain a comprehensive view of the health situation and medical problems of the country and would gain considerable practical experience in social medicine. During the academic year the various teams would report on their activities and observations.

The cost of such field work should not be prohibitive. It seems pretty certain that government funds will be available for medical education after the war and they could not be better spent than on a project that would benefit education and at the same time provide much needed services to the country.

C. Summary of the Course According to Subjects
[The Roman numerals indicate the year.]

I. Social Sciences and Humanities.

INTRODUCTION TO MEDICINE	I
THE PHYSICIAN IN SOCIETY	VI
SOCIAL MEDICINE	V
LANGUAGES AND LITERATURE	I-II
HISTORY OF SCIENCE	I
HISTORY OF MEDICINE	II
PHILOSOPHY	I
SOCIAL ANTHROPOLOGY	II
SOCIOLOGY OF MEDICINE	III
ECONOMICS OF MEDICINE	IV
MEDICO-SOCIOLOGICAL CONFERENCE	V-VI
FIELD WORK	

II. Natural Sciences.

MATHEMATICS	I
BIOSTATISTICS	II
PHYSICS	I
CHEMISTRY	I-II
PHYSIOLOGICAL CHEMISTRY	II-III
PHARMACOLOGY	IV
BIOLOGY	I
PSYCHOBIOLOGY	II
ANATOMY	II-III
PHYSICAL ANTHROPOLOGY	II
PHYSIOLOGY	II-III
PATHOLOGY	III-IV
BACTERIOLOGY	III
FORENSIC MEDICINE	VI
CLINICAL-PATHOLOGICAL CONFERENCE	V-VI
FIELD WORK	

III. Hygiene, Public Health, Social Medicine.

BIOSTATISTICS	II
BACTERIOLOGY	III

IV. Clinical Medicine.

CLINICAL-PATHOLOGICAL CONFERENCE . . . V-VI
MEDICO-SOCIOLOGICAL CONFERENCE . . . . V-VI
FIELD WORK

IV. COURSES FOR AUXILIARY MEDICAL PERSONNEL

Program will have to be worked out.

V. POSTGRADUATE COURSES

Program will have to be worked out.

VI. ORGANIZATION OF THE SCHOOL (See Chart on page 125)

Most medical schools in America were founded as departments of universities or became sooner or later connected with universities. The development was significant in that it raised the standard of the schools to that of universities. It undoubtedly is of material benefit for members and students of a medical faculty to be able to live and work in close touch with members and students of other faculties.

In most cases, however, this cooperation is made impossible, or at least very difficult by the fact that university and medical schools are located either in different cities or in different sections of a city so that the connection is merely administrative.

A new medical school, unless it can be affiliated with a first-rate university and built on the same campus, may be organized as an independent academic unit with the following structure:

1. *Board of Trustees.*

In charge of financial management, general business matters and appointments, the latter upon recommendation of the Council. The Board should include faculty members.

2. *Dean.*

In charge of all educational matters and matters of policy.

3. *Administrative Director.*

In charge of all administrative matters, subordinated to the Dean.

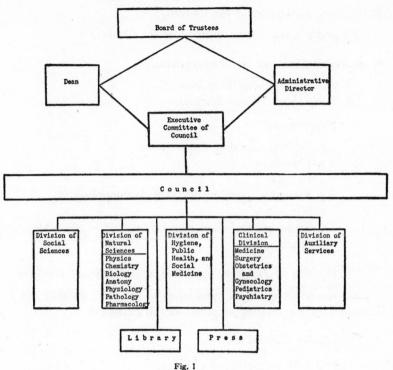

Fig. 1

Organization of School.

4. *Council.*

Consisting of,

Dean, as chairman
Director, as secretary
Heads of Divisions
Heads of Departments
Delegates from all academic ranks
Student delegates
Superintendent of the Hospital
Librarian
Head of Press

The Council shall be a truly democratic body meeting at regular intervals for the discussion of all matters of the School. Since it will be rather large, it shall elect an

5. *Executive Committee of the Council.*

To perform the current business of the Council.

6. *Academic Divisions and Departments.*

I. *Division of Social Sciences.*
II. *Division of Natural Sciences.*

Departments:

1. Physics, including Mathematics
2. Chemistry
3. Biology
4. Anatomy, including Physical Anthropology
5. Physiology
6. Pathology, including Bacteriology and Forensic Medicine
7. Pharmacology

III. *Division of Hygiene, Public Health and Social Medicine.*

No special departments considered as yet. The division can be developed for the training of public health personnel.

IV. *Clinical Division.*

Departments:

1. Medicine
2. Surgery
3. Obstetrics and Gynecology
4. Pediatrics
5. Psychiatry

Clinical specialties will be attached to the various departments.

V. *Division of Auxiliary Services.*

7. *Library.*

8. *Press.*

A new school will probably require a new journal, new text books and monographs. It may be advisable for the school to consider the organization of its own press, unless a university press is available.

I I

The Social Sciences in the Medical School

THE STATEMENT that medicine is a social science sounds like a truism, yet it cannot be repeated often enough because in medical education we still act as if medicine were a natural science and nothing else. There can be no doubt that the target of medicine is to keep individuals adjusted to their environment as useful members of society, or to readjust them when they have dropped out as a result of illness. It is a social goal. Every medical action, moreover, presupposes a relationship between at least two individuals, the patient and the physician, or between two groups, society on one hand, and the medical corps, in the broadest sense of the word, on the other hand.

We can define the function of medicine as consisting of the following four major tasks:

1. The promotion of health
2. The prevention of illness
3. The restoration of the sick
4. Rehabilitation

It is easily apparent that the first, second and fourth tasks require group activities. Health is promoted by providing a decent standard of living, good labor conditions, education, physical culture, means of rest and recreation. The coordinated efforts of large groups are needed to this end, of the statesman, labor, industry, of the educator and of the physician who as an expert in matters of health must define norms and set standards.

The promotion of health obviously tends to prevent illness, yet effective prevention calls for special protective measures such as the protection of large social groups against communicable diseases through the sanitation of dwelling places, quarantine, immunizations, the finding, segregation and treatment of individuals who, suffering from communicable diseases, are a menace to their fellow-men; in other words, the classical tasks of the public health services. Here the

Written in 1945.

state power is called upon to fulfill an extremely important medical function, and the physician acts as a civil servant.

Effective prevention of illness requires further measures for the protection of those groups that are particularly threatened, either physiologically or socially. Specially endangered for physiological reasons are women in pregnancy, childbirth and childbed, are infants and children, and old people. Socially threatened, as a result of their occupation, are industrial workers. Medicine, therefore, had to develop special methods and institutions for the protection of mother and child, for the care of the aged and for the protection of labor. This, however, also required group activities.

Rehabilitation is a function of medicine the importance of which is fully recognized in times of war when society is more keenly aware of its responsibility toward the individuals who sacrifice their health for its protection. We are just beginning to realize that rehabilitation is essential in peacetime also. No medical treatment may be considered completed before the patient has been restored not only physically but also socially. If the disease process has left a disability which renders the individual unable to resume his old place in society, he must be helped to find a new place in which he will continue to be a useful member of society and will maintain not only his earning capacity but his self-respect. A highly differentiated society such as ours could make use of every individual, no matter what his disability might be, provided he had been properly trained for the new task. But this again is a function that requires the cooperative efforts of groups, of physician, educator and government.

Nobody will deny that these three great tasks of medicine are eminently social. The individual appears as a member of a group, and his wants are satisfied by associated action. This is less obvious when we think of a physician treating a patient. Here an individual who suffers from illness seeks the aid of another individual who possesses the knowledge, skill and power to help him. And yet the social elements involved in this seemingly uncomplicated relationship are endless. In taking the history of the patient the physician must inquire into his living and working conditions, into his relationship to the family and other social groups, since social factors may well be responsible for the present illness. Poverty is still the chief cause of disease. In treating the patient, the doctor treats him as an individual but also as a member of a group with his social restoration in mind. In some not infrequent cases the treatment may consist in correcting a social relationship.[1] The surgeon does not merely remove a disease focus but tends to restore the function of an affected organ. The appearance of a scar must be taken into consideration because a disfiguring scar may greatly affect an individual's social life.

As a result of specialization, moreover, medicine is increasingly becoming group medicine practised in health centres. The doctor is no longer alone but one of a group of physicians, nurses, technicians. The patient frequently has to be institutionalized for examination and treatment, in hospitals, sanatoria, convalescent homes where he becomes one in a group of fellow sufferers.

The increased cost of medical care, finally, calls imperatively for some form of group payment so that the economic risk of illness may be spread among large groups and their resources may be pooled.

In view of the fact that medicine has become a social science and that so many other social sciences have entered into its orbit, it is strange to find that these studies scarcely have any place in the curriculum of our medical schools and that students are trained almost exclusively along scientific lines. They are, of course, supposed to have engaged in studies of history, economics, and sociology during their college years, but we all know how superficial these studies are. The science requirements of the so-called premedical curriculum are so heavy that there is little time left for other subjects, particularly if students do not attend a full college course of four years.

Once they enter medical school they devote their first two years to science exclusively, studying anatomy, physiology, physiological chemistry, pathology, bacteriology and pharmacology. The social sciences are non-existent in the program. Some schools offer at that stage courses in medical psychology and vital statistics which could provide a good opportunity to discuss some of the basic laws that govern social intercourse if the instructors were prepared to take advantage of it, but this is rarely the case.

The two clinical years are very crowded and very absorbing. After years of preparation the student finally enters the field of medicine proper and in an incredibly short time he must cover an

[1] Numerous examples are given in G. Canby Robinson, *The Patient as a Person*, New York, 1939 and Henry B. Richardson, *Patients Have Families*, New York, 1945.

enormous territory and must acquire knowledge and skills in internal medicine, surgery, obstetrics and gynecology, pediatrics, psychiatry and all the specialties. Clinical medicine is in many ways applied sociology. Every patient who enters the hospital raises social problems, but the present generation of clinical teachers consists mostly of scientists, brilliant scientists, who are primarily interested in the scientific problem that a patient presents, a problem that has to be solved by scientific means. Social medicine is in most countries still in its infancy.

Disease is a biological process and its immediate causes, the disease-producing factors, are to be sought in the realm of nature. When we speak of poverty as being the chief cause of illness we mean that poverty creates conditions under which an individual cannot lead a life that is conducive to health. Poverty results in malnutrition, poor housing, poor clothing, lack of fuel and therefore in greater exposure to and lowered resistance against physical, chemical and biological factors that become the immediate cause of a given illness. A social maladjustment creates a state of mind that affects the normal physiological functions adversely and may result in disease.

In treating a sick individual the first intention is to remove the immediate cause of his disease, to alleviate symptoms, and in general to aid the natural healing power of the organism. To that end we have to apply methods of science making use of physical, chemical or biological forces.

From all that has been said it is easily apparent that the physician must be trained in the natural sciences, that he must be a scientist. But since the basic causes of many cases of illness are to be found in a man's social environment, since the social factor is never quite absent and since the ultimate goal is the social restoration of the sick, the physician must be trained in the social sciences also. This is particularly necessary today when we possess the means to practise preventive medicine on a large scale, and also because the chronic diseases are in the foreground, in the causation of which social factors play an important part.

Social medicine is not so much a technique as rather an attitude and approach to the problems of medicine, one which I have no doubt will some day permeate the entire curriculum. This, however, will require a new type of clinical teacher and new textbooks.

There have been some interesting new developments in recent years which tend to fill the gap to a certain extent by bringing some social considerations into the curriculum. A number of schools, realizing that the instruction they were offering in hygiene was inadequate, have established Departments of Preventive Medicine. The name is important because it documents the fact that preventive medicine is no longer the prerogative of public health officers but the concern of every practitioner of medicine. These departments are still young and their programs are more or less experimental. Much of their instruction is devoted to the classical subjects of public health, biostatistics, epidemiology, control of exotic diseases and health administration, but beginnings are made to give instruction on economic, social and environmental factors in disease and to assign students to the study of selected patients in order to interest them in the prevention particularly of infectious, nutritional, metabolic and degenerative diseases.

The establishment of such departments was undoubtedly a step in the right direction, one that still offers great possibilities that have hardly been touched yet. Their future will be determined primarily by what personnel will be available. In the beginning they had to be staffed with people who happened to be interested in the subject and were familiar with one or the other aspect of preventive medicine. In the future they will require men equally well trained in medicine, public health and sociology.

Another important development in this direction is represented by the increased attention paid to psychiatry and mental hygiene in medical school curricula. The importance of psychological factors in the genesis and in the course of disease has been recognized at last, and if a demonstration was needed, the present war has certainly revealed the high incidence of mental illness in our society. The psychiatrist cannot study the individual patient in isolation but only as a member of a group in his relationships to other human beings. The psychiatric case history is the elaborate biography of an individual in his social relationships, and in psychiatry even more than in other fields of medicine, social restoration is the true criterion of healing. Psychiatric clinics developed medical social services before other hospitals did because they felt more strongly the need to investigate a patient's environment and to follow him up after he had left the clinic. The study of mental hygiene brings the student in touch with problems of education, asocial behavior, prevention of crime and similar topics which also greatly broaden his outlook. And the psychiatrist in interpreting psychological mechanisms frequently has to draw upon the experiences of the social anthropologist. The Department of Psychiatry in the medical school thus has close affinities to the social sciences.

Forensic medicine or medical jurisprudence plays an important part in the curriculum of European medical schools but is very much neglected in most of our American schools where a few lectures are usually all that is offered to the students. It is an important subject because the administration of the law requires the expert advice of the physician in increasing measure. Its major object is social pathology and it offers great educational opportunities in its combination of physics, chemistry, pathology, psychiatry, jurisprudence and penology.

Thus the social sciences are not entirely absent from the medical school. They have crept in through the back door, more or less haphazardly, and are leading a precarious life. But a beginning has been made that may be developed some day. In the meantime an effort should be made to offer the students more systematic instruction in the social sciences if we want them to be more than mere therapists; if we want to produce the social physician that society will require tomorrow.

In establishing an Institute of the History of Medicine in 1929, the Johns Hopkins University made a definite attempt to create a centre for studies and instruction in the social sciences as related to medicine. Since we now have over fifteen years' experience I may be permitted to discuss briefly the kind of instruction that the Institute is offering.

History of Medicine

A survey undertaken by the American Association of the History of Medicine in 1937 revealed that 54 of 77 medical schools of the United States, or 70 per cent, offered instruction in the history of medicine. In 28 schools the courses were required. In 22 schools the students had a required examination in the subject, while in 6 schools examination was optional or incidental. In the other schools courses were elective.[2]

These figures sound impressive but are somewhat misleading because it is undoubtedly true that the courses offered by many of these schools were of very inferior quality, far below their general standard of instruction. Most schools have accepted the principle that graduate instruction should be given by competent men who are actively engaged in research in their respective fields, but medical history was frequently taught by amateurs who merely reported on what they had read in a current textbook. It is obvious that the value of such instruction is very small. History is too important and too influential a subject to be mishandled in such a way. History moulds the students' minds, and when it is presented irresponsibly it may cause great harm. Whoever teaches psychiatry must be a psychiatrist, and whoever teaches history must be a historian. He may be a physician or a scientist in addition, and as a matter of fact it is a great advantage for him to be a physician, but he must be a historian trained in the methods of historical research.

The content and organization of a course in medical history is largely determined by the group of students to which it is addressed. I found that the best results may be expected if historical instruction is offered at three different levels:

1. *To "premedical" students in the undergraduate school.*

At this level the course assumes the character of an introduction to medicine. The students after having had some teaching in the humanities and social sciences during their first college years are now deeply engaged in the study of science, including biology, physics, chemistry and mathematics. They intend to study medicine and are eager to hear what medicine is, what they may expect from the medical school. The last time I gave such a course I organized it so as to cover the following subjects:

    I. *Man in health*
        1. Man as a mammal
          a. Structure

[2] H. E. Sigerist, Medical history in the medical schools of the United States. *Bull. Hist. Med.*, 1939, 7: 627-662.

b. Function
c. Mind

2. Man as a social being

II. *The promotion of health*

III. *Man in illness*

IV. *Disease*

1. Symptoms
2. Nature
3. Diseases
4. Incidence of illness
5. Social and economic consequences

V. *Causes of disease*

1. Heredity
2. Social environment
3. Physical environment

VI. *Prevention of disease*

VII. *Restoration of health*

1. History of the sick
2. Diagnosis
3. Treatment
4. Rehabilitation

VIII. *Medical practice and the organization of medical services*

IX. *The physician, yesterday, today and tomorrow*

It was a course of 32 hours. The various subjects were developed historically, sociologically and philosophically. I, of course, had to be very elementary as far as medicine was concerned, but the main purpose was to give a general picture of medicine in broad outlines, drawing upon the student's previous experiences in various fields and showing how they would all converge in the study and in the profession of medicine.

I think that such a course can have a great educational value. It gives more purpose to the premedical studies by demonstrating the necessity of a broad, general and scientific foundation. It also is a good preparation for medical school in that it develops in the students a certain attitude towards the subject. The historian of medicine who gives such a course is their first medical teacher and has a great opportunity to advise them on how to organize their studies, and since he meets them at a moment when they are extremely receptive, some of his words will be remembered after many years.

2. *To first-year medical students*

Our Institute offers every year a 16-hour course announced as "Outlines of the History of Medicine." In the previous course the accent was on medicine, and history was brought in more or less as a method or approach, while here the accent is on history. Students come to medical school from a great variety of colleges. They have all met the entrance requirements in science but their preparation in the humanities and social sciences differs a great deal. The course, therefore, presents an opportunity to teach them history, with a strong bias on medicine. The purpose is not to burden them with an infinity of dates and names but to show them what the driving forces of history are, to present some of the great civilizations of the past, discussing their social and economic structure, their health problems, what was done to meet them, how it was done and why it was done in a given way. The discussion obviously includes the part played by individuals and the thoughts that guided their actions. Parallels are drawn constantly between the development of medicine and the development of literature, art, music, the law and other manifestations of civilization so that medicine appears as one aspect of the general civilization of a given period.

Since the course is short a certain selection of topics must be made, and it can be made in such a way that each one will illustrate a certain point. Thus in discussing primitive medicine we can show that some elements of it never die but persist through the centuries and are encountered in our own society in the form of various superstitions. Babylonia presents an opportunity to discuss the relations between medicine and religion and the part played by astrology in the history of thought. The philosophic approach characteristic of Greek medicine may be used as the starting point of a discussion on the influence that philosophy has exerted at all times on the formation of medical systems and on the possibilities and limitations of a philosophic interpretation of the phenomena of health and disease. The Middle Ages are a good example of a period at which the theory and practice of medicine were fully integrated into the general pattern of life and were dominated by theology. The Renaissance illustrates the rebellion against traditional authorities, the birth of a new economic order, the rise of individualism, the discovery of the world and its influence upon science. In analyzing Harvey's discovery of the circulation of the blood we discuss the significance of the experimental method in medical science. The Industrial Revolution demonstrates how economic developments affected the health and medical situation of the Western world. This is the place to discuss the significance of tools in the evolution of medicine, the creation of a new medical technology that calls for new forms of medical service.

The purpose of the course is to open up horizons, to make the students think, to help them to understand what they are doing and to make them realize that medicine cannot be studied in isolation, that it is one part of a great and indivisible whole.

The course is supplemented every year by an 8-hour course on the "History of American Medicine" because American students should be familiar with the development in their own country and should know at what point of it they stand. In addition to that, a number of lectures are offered every year to beginners on "Greek and Latin Terminology in Modern Medicine" and on "Medical Bibliography."

3. *To advanced medical students*

A medical school that has an organized department of the history of medicine will not only offer didactic courses for beginners but will provide opportunities for advanced studies in the field. Our Institute is holding every year a number of seminar courses on various subjects. Looking over the annual reports of the department I find that the following courses have been given during the last ten years:

Problems and methods of medical history
Ancient medicine from Homer to the end of antiquity
Religious and scientific medicine in Greece and Rome
History of Graeco-Roman science
Problems of Graeco-Roman medicine and science
Hellenistic medicine

History of ancient anatomy and physiology
Medical education and ethics in antiquity
Reading and interpretation of Greek medical and scientific texts
Hippocratic medicine
The Aphorisms of Hippocrates
The Aristotelian system of biology
The ancient Peripatos and the development of ancient science
Aristotle and the rise of modern biology
Plato's physiology
Medical monographs in China
Pediatrics in China
History of anatomy and anatomical illustrations
History of physiology
Historical introduction to pathology
Pathology in the 19th century
History of pharmacology
History of therapeutics
Historical introduction to clinical medicine
History of clinical diagnosis
History of hygiene and public health
History of psychiatry since Pinel
History of surgery
History of surgery in the 19th century
History of iatrochemistry
Medicine in utopias
The historical foundations of the present world conflict
Research seminar and research conference (discussion of current historical research of the department)

SOCIOLOGY AND ECONOMICS OF MEDICINE

It may be assumed that medical students have had some elementary instruction in general sociology and economics during their early college years. The task of the medical school is to refresh their memory and to teach them in what way disease affects social life and by what measures society protects itself against disease. A department such as ours, obviously, does not attempt to teach the practice of social medicine but rather its theory, the sociology of medicine. There are various ways of doing this. The field is still young and during the past ten years we have been experimenting a great deal. At present I am teaching the subject in two different types of courses.

Every few years I give a systematic course of 32 hours, announced as "Introduction to the Sociology and Economics of Medicine," addressed to students of the School of Medicine and of the School of Hygiene and Public Health. It has never been twice the same because I am developing it constantly, but it covers the following subjects:

I. *Foundations*
    1. Structure of an industrial society
    2. The new technology of medicine

II. *The incidence of illness*
    1. Recent changes in the incidence of illness
    2. Social distribution of illness

III. *Supply and distribution of medical personnel and equipment*
    1. Physicians (general practitioners and specialists), dentists, nurses, technicians, etc.
    2. Hospitals, sanatoria, laboratories, etc.
    3. Public health services
    4. Industrial health services

IV. *The costs of illness*
    1. Costs of medical care
        a. Costs of personnel (incomes of physicians, dentists, etc.)
        b. Hospital economics
        c. Costs of drugs and appliances
        d. Miscellaneous expenditures
    2. Loss of wages
    3. Capital losses through premature deaths

V. *Methods to meet the costs of illness*
    1. Voluntary insurance
        a. Mutual benefit societies
        b. Commercial insurance
        c. Private group clinics with prepayment plans
        d. Cooperative health associations
        e. Group hospitalization (Blue Cross)
        f. Medical service plans of medical societies
        g. Rural health plans under the Federal Government
    2. Compulsory insurance
        a. History, principles, scope
        b. Groups covered
        c. Benefits
        d. Cost, premiums, remuneration of physicians
        e. Administration

3. Public services
    a. Expansion of public health services
    b. From Zemstvo to Soviet medicine
VI. *Recent trends in medical organization*
    1. Group practice
    2. Health centres
    3. Health districts
    4. Special problems of rural health services
    5. Democratic control of health services
VII. *Critical summary and outlook*

I think that such a course fills a gap in the curriculum of the medical school. It discusses problems that every physician will have to face sooner or later and that are usually not touched by other departments.

As was mentioned before, the course is not offered every year. I am giving instead seminar courses announced as "Problems in the Sociology and Economics of Medicine." The choice of subjects discussed in these seminars is determined primarily by current events and by field work in which I am engaged at the time. The students take an active part in the course, presenting reports which then are discussed critically. Current legislation is usually reported in the press, lay and medical, in a partisan spirit, and I am anxious to have the students read the bills and other documents and form their own judgment. To give an example, the Seminar of 1944-45 discussed among others the following subjects:

Interim Reports from the Subcommittee on Wartime Health and Education to the Committee on Education and Labor, U.S. Senate (Pepper Committee).

Hill-Burton Bill, S.191. Hospital Construction Act.

The 11 Health Insurance Bills introduced before the California State Assembly and Senate in January, 1945.

Health services in the Shipyards of Henry J. Kaiser.

Better Health for Rural America. Proposed "National Statement" on Rural Health and Sanitation of the Interbureau Committee on Post-War Programs, U.S. Department of Agriculture. February 1, 1945.

Medical Care in a National Health Program. Official Statement of the American Public Health Association, adopted October 4, 1944.

Principles of a Nation-Wide Health Program. Committee of 29.

A National Health Service. White Paper of the British Ministry of
Health, of 1944 (Cmd. 6502).

Report of Inter-Departmental Committee on Medical Schools (Good-
enough Report). British Ministry of Health (S.O. Code No. 32-363).

Report of the National Health Services Commission on the Provision
of an organized National Health Service for all sections of the
People of the Union of South Africa (U.G. No. 30, 1944).

New Developments in the Health Services of New Zealand.

Health Services in the Canadian Province of Saskatchewan.

When the Wagner-Murray-Dingell Bill to establish a Unified
National Social Insurance System (S. 1161 and H.R. 2861) was before
the Committee on Finance of the Senate I devoted an entire seminar
of 32 hours to a study of social security legislation with special emphasis
on health insurance so that the students would have sufficient knowledge and background to form an independent opinion on the bill
and what it would mean to the American people. In a previous
seminar we had devoted considerable time to the study of the
Beveridge Plan, the Report of the Advisory Committee on Health
Insurance of the Canadian Government, and the Report on Security,
Work and Relief Policies of our National Resources Planning Board.

Other seminars were devoted to a study of certain areas. Thus
we once had a seminar on health conditions and medical facilities
in the State of Maryland. Each one of 23 students had a county
assigned to him and 6 students surveyed the city. They presented
detailed reports on their findings in which they analyzed the population, occupations, social and economic conditions, with maps of
every county on which the location of every doctor, dentist, nurse,
hospital and other facilities were marked in. They were also encouraged to make recommendations on ways and means to improve
existing services, and to estimate the costs of such improvements.
Whenever I returned from a study tour in Europe, Africa or Asia
I devoted part of a seminar to the discussion of problems I had
encountered and work I had done, so that the students would benefit
by my own experience. I once gave an entire course on "The Protection of Health in the Soviet Union."

One advantage of these courses is that they are usually attended
by students from various schools. Students of the School of Medicine
and of the School of Hygiene and Public Health are, as a rule, repre-

sented in equal proportion, and we frequently have students of economics, sociology or political science. Sometimes the courses are also attended by faculty members and members of the State Department of Health. The courses thus assume a strongly interdepartmental character, and I find that such a collaboration of students with a widely different range of experience is extremely stimulating and fertile.

The program is planned in such a way that a student in the course of four years is given an opportunity to learn a great deal in the field of sociology and economics of medicine.

PHILOSOPHY OF MEDICINE

Instruction in the philosophy of medicine represents a new development in the program of our Institute. We never intended to give special courses in the subject, particularly since we felt that many of our historical and sociological courses implicitly had a philosophical character.

When we became involved in the war there was a sudden spontaneous demand for instruction in philosophy on the part of our medical students. They had been greatly stirred by the war and the part they were to play in it and were groping for philosophical guidance. Our first impulse was to refer them to the Department of Philosophy of the University, but the department had collapsed because its few members had been called to the armed forces, and the University made no effort to provide instruction in a subject that was more needed at that time than ever. And so our department had to help if the students were not to be disappointed. We were fortunate in having a man on our staff who was a good philosopher and was prepared and willing to give a course. He has been giving it every year, very successfully. The subject is developed historically with a bias on medicine, making use of the experience of the physician. The response from our student body was excellent and a rather whimsical phenomenon occurred, namely, that students from the philosophical faculty came to the medical school for instruction in philosophy and that our professor, a member of the medical faculty, was invited to give an—unofficial—course in philosophy to the students of the English Department.

We do not know yet what we shall do after the war but we have plans to develop a course in "Ethics of Medicine." In most medical schools graduating students are given a few lectures usually announced as "Medical Ethics." As a rule these lectures have no relation to ethics in a philosophical sense but discuss medical etiquette and bedside manners. A course that would approach the subject historically and philosophically and would discuss the various spheres that determine the physician's behavior would without any doubt have great educational value.

*

The Johns Hopkins Institute of the History of Medicine, quite apart from the research activities in which it is engaged, represents an interesting educational experiment in its attempt to bring the social sciences into the medical school. All its courses are elective, most of them are held at late evening hours, yet they are all well attended, which shows that there is a demand for them. Almost all students attend the elementary courses; many, in addition, take part in a seminar or two, and every year a number of students graduate from our school who during the four years of their studies have attended practically all the courses that the Institute has offered during that time. I keep in close touch with many of them because I became attached to them and also because I am interested to see the results of our teaching. There is a growing demand for men and women who have undergone this kind of training, particularly from the part of organized medical services and government agencies. It is very gratifying to see that these doctors have a much broader approach to the problems of medicine and public health than the average physician and that they are doing excellent work in all sections of this country and in many foreign lands.

The day may come when the social approach to medicine will so permeate the entire curriculum that much of our present teaching will become superfluous. In the meantime, however, I think that a department devoted to the social sciences in the medical school has an important function to fulfill.

12

The History of Science in Postwar Education

THERE can be no doubt that the history of science as a subject of instruction has been greatly neglected in the past and is still very much neglected today. Few of our great universities offer any courses at all, and among them a very few offer adequate instruction.

There was a time, not so long ago, when studies in the history of science were considered an unnecessary luxury, a hobby for retired scientists. Science was progressing rapidly, was becoming increasingly complicated and specialized, and everybody was looking ahead into the future. It seemed useless to look into the past and seemed wasteful to burden the students with historical considerations.

The attitude toward the history of science is changing rapidly, for reasons that we shall discuss in a moment. Leading scientists, historians and educators, presidents of great universities have come out openly in favor of instruction in the history of science and have repeatedly emphasized the great educational value of such studies.

They talked, beautifully, but as a rule did not act. When you have a chance to discuss these matters with such an educator and you ask him quite candidly why he does not provide, in his school, instruction in a field that he considers so important, you invariably hear the same answers. One is that funds were not available. Yet funds were available for many other purposes, and wherever there is a sound constructive program and the determination to carry it out, funds usually come forth.

Another and more serious answer is that the school intended to provide instruction in the history of science but could not find the right man to teach the subject. And in such a case the educator will usually add: "Why do you not train the people that we so urgently need?"

Address of the retiring vice-president of Section L, American Association for the Advancement of Science, presented at the meeting in Cleveland on September 12, 1944.

To this very justified and challenging question we reply that it is difficult to encourage young people to enter into a field in which so far there have been no outlets. A man has to make a living, and after many years of highly specialized training in the history of science, he usually ends up teaching elementary biology or chemistry or Latin in a college, and his training remains unused. If universities had chairs for the history of science, then, of course, we would be only too eager to train people for these positions. The problem, in other words, reverts to the old proposition whether the egg or the hen comes first.

There is, however, another and much more disturbing aspect to the question, namely, that it is becoming increasingly difficult, particularly in this country, to find young people who possess the elementary equipment required for studies in the history of science. We expect as a matter of course that a historian of philosophy have a profound understanding of philosophy but be at the same time fully trained in methods of historical research. A historian of music must understand music but must be a historian as well. The same requirement obviously applies to the historian of science. He must understand science. We do not expect him to be equally competent in astronomy, botany and chemistry, but he must know at least one field of science thoroughly. And he must be a historian in addition, that is, he must be able to read and evaluate and interpret historical sources.

In view of the fact that ancient science dominated the Western world for over two thousand years and that Latin remained the language of science for several centuries thereafter, it is pretty obvious that the historian of science who wants to work from first-hand sources, who wants to teach the subject and to guide student research must know Greek and Latin, and must know these languages well. It is not enough for him to be able to decipher a Latin text; he must be able to read it. Of course, it would be good for him to know also Arabic and half a dozen other languages, but a thorough knowledge of Greek and Latin is a minimum requirement for a man who wants to become an academic teacher in the history of science.

We all know that it is very difficult to-day to find young people who are equally well trained in the humanities and in science. It was different in the past when the humanities were the gateway to university studies. This is why in the nineteenth century great scientists and physicians, men like Berthelot, Du Bois-Reymond, Virchow and many others were able to make important contributions to the history of science. When they became interested in the history of their field, they had a background from which they could draw. Today the scientist who becomes interested in history encounters almost insurmountable barriers. He is unable to read the basic texts, has to rely on translations and on secondary sources. In my own field, the history of medicine, a number of disgraceful books have been published recently that would have been inconceivable one or two generations ago. They were written by very competent doctors who, however, had not had the slightest humanistic training, had no appreciation of the historian's responsibility and were totally unable to distinguish between good and bad sources.

Young people who come to us for training have usually had a few years of high-school Latin and no Greek at all. Their knowledge of general history is extremely scanty. They can, of course, learn Greek and Latin and general history at the university, and we urge them to do it. But the result is that the time that should be spent for specialized training actually has to be spent in acquiring the most elementary tools. Our Johns Hopkins Institute of the History of Medicine offers the degrees of M.A. and Ph.D. in medical history, but in twelve years we have given only one M.A. degree and no Ph.D. We had candidates, but most of them gave up after a while realizing that their preparation was hopelessly inadequate.

And yet, in spite of these undeniable difficulties, we are fortunate in having in the United States today a number of scholars who are fully prepared to fill chairs of the history of science. George Sarton, the foremost authority in the field, has been active in this country for more than a quarter of a century and has developed a flourishing school. Scattered all over the country, in various positions, are young people, scientists, philosophers, philologists and historians who in spite of sometimes considerable difficulties have become very competent in some field of the history of science. What they need is a few years of leisure without academic duties that they could spend with Sarton at Harvard or in some similar centre. This would give them an opportunity to accomplish a solid piece of research and to broaden their training whereupon, I am sure, many of them would be prepared to teach the history of science competently.

An interesting and promising experiment in this direction was undertaken recently by the Johns Hopkins University. In 1940, the university with the aid of the Carnegie Corporation created two Carnegie Fellowships in the History of Graeco-Roman Science. They were each for two years and carried an annual stipend of $2,000 with the usual privileges granted to research fellows. The idea was to steer young classical philologists into the field of ancient science where so much remains to be done, so that later while teaching the classics they would devote their researches to the history of science and would also be able to teach the subject.

When the fellowships were announced, we received over 20 applications. The two candidates accepted were both doctors of philosophy in classics, and in addition one of them was an excellent mathematician and physicist who had already published a number of papers, while the other had engaged in studies of botany. The two fellows were attached to the Institute of the History of Medicine. They attended all courses of the department and took an active part in the seminars. As a matter of fact, the research seminar was turned over to them repeatedly for a number of weeks, so that they had an opportunity to present their problems in detail and to have them discussed. One was working on Theophrastus, the other on Caelius Aurelianus and on several other problems. Both were also permitted to teach in a postgraduate course that the department gave in 1942.

The war somewhat interfered with the program, in that one fellow interrupted his work after one year to take a position with the Navy. The other, however, completed his two years very successfully. He is a solid researcher and excellent teacher who, in my opinion, would be an asset to the faculty of any university. I very much hope that these fellowships will be resumed after the war and possibly even extended, because they seem to be a step in the right direction. It is obvious that not every college can have a department of the history of science, but every one has a department of classics, and to have one man in such a department who combines classics with science and is prepared to teach the history of science should prove to be a great advantage.

At any rate, competent teaching personnel is available today, not in large but in sufficient number to make a start, and it is therefore up to the schools to take the next step by creating teaching positions.

Once they are available, without any doubt more personnel will be trained.

*

A great deal of planning is being done today, and this is a very sound symptom. It shows that we are trying to learn from the experience of the war. We feel that much was wrong, in many fields, in the pre-war world, and we endeavor to improve conditions by planning intelligently for the postwar world which, we feel, must and will be different.

The war has revealed dramatically the inadequacy of our educational system. Not only has it shown that with 341,200 registrants rejected for military service (up to September 1, 1943) for being unable "to read and write the English language as well as a student who has completed four years in an American grammar school," we have an amount of illiteracy for which there is no excuse in a democracy, but the mere fact that we did nothing to prevent this war is an indictment of our educational system. We can not blame the politicians, because their actions are determined by public opinion, and public opinion is the result of the educational status of the population.

Whenever we have an opportunity to probe into the present situation, we find appalling conditions. A poll conducted in July, 1943, revealed that in spite of all means of information, newspapers, radio, movies, 79 per cent of the population had never heard that at that time there was a hotly contested National Social Insurance Act before Congress, a bill which, if passed, would have taken 6 per cent of all wages and would have given the people great social security benefits. The poll showed that 84 per cent of the farm population had never heard of the bill, one which for the first time included farm laborers. This reveals a lack of education in citizenship that is simply staggering. How can we expect a democracy to function effectively if the majority of the citizens take no interest in some of the most vital issues that concern their own security? And what is to blame but our educational system? Education in citizenship, however, presupposes an intelligent teaching of history.

A survey conducted by *The New York Times* several years ago revealed that thousands of young people graduate from colleges every year with a bachelor's degree without having had any instruction in the history of their own country. How can we expect them to become enlightened citizens prepared to take an active part in determining the destinies of the nation?

It seems that many people still consider the study of history some kind of a luxury. Oh, they will gladly admit that it is interesting to know what happened in the past, and how people lived in the early days. They will concede that an educated person should have some knowledge of history, but after all we are living in today's world with its hard realities, in ever changing situations and, they usually add, nobody has ever learned from history.

At this very moment important inter-allied conferences are being held at which plans are elaborated for reshaping the world. They are attended by statesmen and diplomatists with staffs of experts in economics, geography and other fields, but it is striking to see that historians are hardly ever consulted. Historians are considered as college professors who know all about the past but, of course, have no idea of the world in which they live.[1]

Nothing could be more erroneous than such an attitude. History is not a luxury. The knowledge and views we have of our past are the most powerful driving forces in our life. Every situation in which we find ourselves, every event that takes place, whether it be a world war, a revolution, a strike or merely the enactment of a city ordinance, are all the results of certain developments and trends. We are usually not aware of them and are therefore often surprised when the event takes place. The historical analysis that makes these developments and trends conscious, that reveals the factors that have led to a given situation, permits us to understand what is happening around us and helps us to act more intelligently.

The study of history must be given a prominent place in postwar education if we are determined to train not only specialists but citizens of a democracy. This has been recognized in various quarters, and efforts are being made to give history more hours in the curriculum. Criticism of existing conditions, however, has been more along quantitative than qualitative lines. Much has been said about the number of courses and hours the students should have, yet it is obvious

---

[1] There may be another reason why statesmen often distrust historians. They know that sooner or later they will have to appear before the tribunal of history and that the judgment of just such historians will determine whether their descendants will be proud or ashamed of them.

that a great deal depends on what kind of historical instruction is being offered. And this is where the history of science comes in.

*

Science has played such a tremendous part in shaping our world and is bound to play an increasingly important part in the world of to-morrow that it is impossible to understand historical developments without considering science. It is strange, therefore, that there are still many text-books of history in which the word science hardly occurs.

The time is fortunately gone when the teaching of history centered around dynastic quarrels, boundary disputes and wars. We are primarily interested in the history of man's achievements and creations, in the history of that broad complex of phenomena commonly called civilization. Man's efforts to understand and master nature certainly represent one very important aspect of it. We do not neglect to study the many factors that have advanced or retarded the development of civilization. Dynastic quarrels, boundary disputes and wars may have been such factors and therefore will not be overlooked. The basic importance of economic factors is generally recognized, and history has in many hands become primarily economic history. Economic history, however, must always consider the history of man's tools, of his technology, and technology is to a large extent the result of science.

Science has not only revolutionized our economic life but has also profoundly influenced our views of life, our religion, philosophy, literature and art. It is impossible to understand the naturalist school without knowing Claude Bernard, the physiologist. The influence of Darwin is still widely felt. In other words, from whatever angle we approach history we are bound to encounter sooner or later the phenomenon, science.

The historical analysis will also explain the frustrations of science. Why is it that in times of war we are willing to make free use of science, while as soon as peace is achieved we refuse, or so far at least have refused, to apply principles of science to the basic processes of social life, to production, distribution and consumption?

If the teaching of history is to be more than an intellectual recreation, if it is meant to help young people to understand the world in which they live and to play their part in it intelligently, it must by necessity include the history of science, which must become an integral part of all phases of historical instruction.

Today universities only, and only a few, offer instruction in the history of science, but I feel very strongly that in postwar education the teaching of the history of science should begin in the primary school. At that stage the biographical approach may be the most appropriate. Children are interested in nature and in technology; the story of the great scientists and of their discoveries, presented in simple terms, would be most inspiring. I first heard the name of Benjamin Franklin in my French school when I was seven years old. Our teacher, an old lady—she may not have been so old, but to us she seemed so—told us about the great American who had come to France, and she described his experiments with a kite and his invention of the lightning rod. She also told us about his stove. We were so impressed that although it was a very long time ago, I remember that class as vividly as if it had been yesterday. And we never flew kites without thinking of Franklin. When we were struggling with the multiplication table we heard about Pythagoras because in France the multiplication table is called *la table de Pythagore*. Later at the age of about ten, we learned a great deal about Linnaeus because we were gathering plants and were grouping them according to families. We built a sun-dial in the school garden as the Babylonians and Chinese had done thousands of years ago.

Today boys and girls are very keen on building airplanes. This presents a great opportunity to tell them about Leonardo da Vinci. I am sure that a class devoted to Leonardo with lantern slides showing some of his machines and also his paintings would make a lasting impression on children. And the history of flying from Leonardo to the Wright brothers makes a fascinating story.

Much history of science can be taught in the primary school in such an informal way. It not only adds color to the teaching and is inspiring, but also gives young people a certain historical perspective and respect for the past. They come to realize that it is not accidental that they enjoy the fruits of science, but it is the result of the labor and genius of generations of men who preceded them.

In high school, instruction will be more systematic. One may consider giving a special course in the history of science wherein

The History of Science in Postwar Education

Sir William Cecil Dampier's new book, "A Shorter History of Science" (New York: Macmillan, 1944), will be found equally useful by teachers and students. I hear that in England the introduction of the subject into the curriculum of the grammar school is being considered very seriously.

Whether a special course is given or not, the history of science should, in the secondary school, become an integral part of the teaching of history as well as of science. In other words, a study of ancient history should not be limited to the history of political events and economic conditions, but should also picture the development and the contributions of ancient civilization of which science was an essential part. A history of Elizabethan England that ignores science remains fragmentary by necessity. A certain knowledge of Elizabethan science is needed for the mere understanding of Shakespeare's plays. Good examples of historical text-books that include science, at least to a certain extent, are James H. Breasted's "Ancient Times, a History of the Early World" and Carl L. Becker's "Modern History, The Rise of a Democratic, Scientific and Industrialized Civilization."

The teaching of science, on the other hand, can gain a great deal if the historical approach is used as a didactic method. The teacher will soon find that there is no better way of making complicated matters clear to the student than by presenting the subject genetically. The history of oxidation discussed in a course of chemistry or the history of the circulation of the blood in a biology course enables one to explain and clarify a great many basic concepts. And in presenting a subject historically, the science teacher can draw the attention of his students to philosophical problems. He can impress upon them that physics and chemistry are not a collection of rules and formulae but are an attempt to understand and interpret nature.

The need for instruction in the history of science in colleges is so obvious that it hardly requires any elaboration. If the purpose of the undergraduate school is to give young people a broad general education and to help them to understand the world in which they live and in which they are called upon to play a part, the course must include both the humanities and the sciences.

Students as a rule feel more attracted to one or the other field, and many enter school having a definite major subject in mind whereby they are inclined to neglect the other fields. It should be impressed upon them, however, that science and the humanities are not two separate worlds. In the past, philosophy was the connecting link, and there is no reason why it should not be today. Unfortunately many professional philosophers have developed an ivory tower attitude and a language that nobody understands who does not belong to the brotherhood. They have lost contact with the realities, and thus have lost their grip on students. The history of science that combines the humanities, the social and the natural sciences, and is philosophic in outlook could to a certain extent fill the gap and take the place in college education that philosophy once held.

I think that every college should make an effort to provide not only some but competent and thorough instruction in the field. Courses should be supplemented by seminars in which the students would be encouraged to read and study texts, classics of science. Unfortunately we have not a series of classics comparable to Ostwald's "Klassiker der exakten Naturwissenschaften," but many texts are available in English translation. We also have intelligent text-books such as Sir William Cecil Dampier's "A History of Science and its Relations with Philosophy and Religion" (Cambridge, 3rd ed., 1942) and Charles Singer's "A Short History of Science to the Nineteenth Century" (Oxford, 1941).

In the graduate school, finally, the history of science has an extremely important function to fulfill. The graduate school is training specialists, physicists, chemists, bacteriologists, engineers, physicians, etc. Knowledge has accumulated tremendously in science with the result that every scientific discipline has become extremely complicated and specialized. The danger is obvious that we train mere technicians, men highly competent and highly skilled in one limited field of science but unaware of the social function of science and unprepared to play their part as citizens.

At the time of the great depression, I was once standing on the Grand Coulee Dam while it was under construction and was shown around by an agricultural engineer. Pointing to the waste land, he gave me a glowing picture of how irrigation would turn this desert into a flourishing garden, how at my next visit I would find miles and miles of the finest orchards producing the best fruit in the world. When I asked quite naively who was going to eat this fruit, his answer was, "That's none of my business." The thought had never occurred to him that the fine fruit produced by so much labor and skill might be left rotting on the trees because so far we had been unable to organize distribution and consumption along scientific lines. And yet he was a citizen of a democracy who had had the best possible education, whose voice might have been very influential.

Today when science is having such a strong impact upon the life of society, the scientist can no longer afford to remain cloistered in his laboratory and let the world be damned. He must assume responsibilities toward the community and must take an active part in determining the destinies of the nation. This, however, requires a broader training than he had in the past. Instruction in the history, sociology and philosophy of science, by teaching him humanities and social sciences in a language he understands, will open his eyes to many problems and will undoubtedly contribute toward making him a better scientist and a better citizen.

The graduate school is also training historians, philologists, philosophers, economists, sociologists who must have some knowledge of science and must be familiar with its history. The historian of science who is both scientist and historian is best prepared to interpret science for them, presenting it in a language they understand.

The great educational value of the history of science is gradually being recognized, in England probably more than in the United States. But in this country, more and more educators are also beginning to realize that education at all levels can be broadened and enriched considerably by giving history a more prominent place in the curriculum and by including the history of science.

The war has ruthlessly destroyed many values; but just as it has cleared slums and made room for better housing, it has also cleared or at least exposed educational slums and has opened the way for improvements. It is to be hoped that in planning for postwar education, the men who are at the head of our great institutions of learning will avail themselves of the opportunities that the history of science offers for training the citizens of to-morrow.

Outlook

WHILE I am writing these lines, in the spring of 1945, victory is in sight. The Nazi monster is crumbling at last, defeated by the superior manpower and industrial potential of the United Nations, by intelligent military leadership and the heroism and sacrifice of untold millions of men and women.

It will be a great day when organized resistance ceases in Europe, and the fate of Japan can easily be foreseen. And then?

And then we shall first of all realize how much poorer we all have become. We shall be appalled at the sight of the ruins, physical and moral, that the war has wrought all over the world.

And then we shall have to reconstruct the world upon new foundations so as to prevent a further catastrophe that we could hardly survive. Shall we be able to muster the intelligence and courage that the task requires? What we have seen so far has not been very encouraging. Fascism is by no means dead and cannot be killed with physical weapons. The tendency of governments to revert to the status quo, to the very conditions that caused the war, is all too marked. The best conceived security organization cannot possibly function if it is merely superimposed upon rotten and outdated social and economic structures.

The universities will have a tremendous part to play in the reconstruction of the world. They failed yesterday, are shattered today; will they be better prepared tomorrow? Some institutions have already announced their postwar programs, and again what we have heard did not sound encouraging. The trend seems to be toward utilitarianism, acceleration, toward development in width and not in depth.

Still, there is no reason for despair. The war is by no means over. It will gradually evolve into its revolutionary phase, into the struggle between progress and reaction. The millions of oppressed people in Europe and Asia have hardly been heard yet. Stunned by years of starvation and slavery, they have not yet been able to assert themselves. They will come to the fore and will take their destinies into their own hands.

There can be no doubt as to the final outcome of the present conflict although nobody can foretell how many years the process will take. This is an age of democracy. The common men, the laborers in factory and farm, the office workers, the scientists and the scholars, they will shape the world of tomorrow and will create the institutions of learning that every nation needs.

Acknowledgments

The address, *The History of Science in Postwar Education,* was first published in *Science,* 1944, Vol. 100, pp. 415-420 and is reprinted with the permission of the publisher.

The following addresses and essays were first published in the *Bulletin of the History of Medicine* and are reprinted with the permission of the Johns Hopkins Institute of the History of Medicine:

> *University Education,* 1940, Vol. VIII, pp. 3-21
>
> *War and Culture,* 1942, Vol. XI, pp. 1-11
>
> *On the Threshold of Another Year of War,* 1943, Vol. XIII, pp. 1-9
>
> *Commemorating Andreas Vesalius,* 1943, Vol. XIV, pp. 541-546
>
> *The University's Dilemma,* 1943, Vol. XIV, pp. 1-13
>
> *The University at the Crossroads,* 1944, Vol. XV, pp. 233-245
>
> *The Study of Medicine in Wartime,* 1944, Vol. XV, pp. 1-13
>
> *Classics of Medicine,* 1944, Vol. XVI, pp. 1-12
>
> *Trends in Medical Education,* 1941, Vol. IX, pp. 177-198

Index

Index

Index

Group medicine, 114, 129
Guernica, 4
Gynecology, 119 f., 123, 130

H

Haeckel, Ernst Heinrich, 13 f.
Haldane, J. B. S., 28
Hale-White, Sir William, 93
Haller, Albrecht von, 59, 96
Halsted, W. S., 80
Hammar, J. August, 97
Harvey, William, 93, 136
Health, attitude toward, 83, 86; center, 113 f., 121, 129; insurance, 75, 112
Helmholtz, Hermann von, 96, 100
Henle, Jacob, 97, 100
Heredity, 100
Hippocrates, 93, 94, 95, 137
Hirschfeld, H., 14
History, 12 f., 34 f., 60; American, 147 f.; economic, 149; of civilization, 102 f.; of medicine, 17, 19 ff., 49 ff., 103, 118, 122, 132-135, 145; of philosophy, 103; of science, 19, 33, 118, 122, 143-153
Hitler, Adolf, 3, 21, 34, 39, 58
Holland, 55
Homer, 136
Hormones, 111
Hospital, 85, 89, 108 f., 113, 129, 131
Housing, 119, 123
Howell, W. H., 81
Humanism, 13
Humanities, 8, 36 f., 57, 58, 60, 104, 133, 144, 151 f.
Hygiene, 60, 109, 131; school, 120, 123

I

Ideal, educational, 107; medical, 107
Ignorance, 51
Illiteracy, 147
Illness, incidence of, 111; mental, 131
Imperialism, 39, 44
India, 46
Indoctrination, 69

Industrial, hygiene, 120, 123; medicine, 103
Industrialization, 74
Infant welfare, 120, 123
Influenza, 18
Institute of the History of Medicine, at Leipzig, 20 f.; at Johns Hopkins, *see* Johns Hopkins University
Internship, 110
Ireland, 46
Isis, 17
Islam, 46
Italy, 36, 39, 46, 50, 59, 86

J

Japan, 4 f., 35, 39
Jenner, Edward, 100
Johns Hopkins Hospital, 108
Johns Hopkins University, 22, 146; Institute of the History of Medicine, 22 f., 41, 91, 93, 106, 132 ff., 145 f.; School of Hygiene and Public Health, 80; School of Medicine, 55, 80 ff., 108 ff., 115
Jones, Claude E., 96
Jones, W. H. S., 94
Jurisprudence, medical, 132

K

Kaiser, Henry J., 139
Kant, Immanuel, 13
Kelly, Emerson C., 94, 95
Kelly, Howard A., 81
Keyes, Thomas E., 93
King's College, London, 14
Koch, Robert, 100
Kutusov, 34

L

Labor, 39, 128; conditions, 103, 127; market, 74, 112
Laboratory, 25, 81, 84
Laënnec, R. Théophile H., 93

Index

Index

Index